READER FEEDBACK:

"I can't tell you how your book has helped. I have read it probably four times and highlighted tons of passages. It is the best book on the subject right now. Everything I started to wonder about was answered in the next chapter. You are real and I can relate."
  -Joy R.

"I'm on my 7th day and I have to say that this really is life changing to see such a notable difference in m e. I have lived in a vicious cycle of being aggressively hungry and trying to work around it, deny it, give in to it, and get fat and depressed and irritable - reading your book was eerie because everything you said seemed to showcase me. Thank you so much for the honesty and the no fluff and hype approach to a subject that is very real to many."
  –Stephanie S.

"I have now began what I hope to be a sugar free life, and I when I stumble, when there is a cloud of overwhelming confusion, when it just seems impossible, I think of your words, and I give myself a pat on the back."
  –Stefania

"I really enjoyed reading your book. It was easy to read, and I have been very successful with overcoming my sugar addiction since reading the book."
  –Bonnie

"You've captured all my feelings, emotions and constant battles (within myself) for these last 3 years. Since banishing as much sugar as possible, I've noticed I am a much calmer, focused and balanced individual– I no longer crave sugar and the daily constant yo-yo diets and self sabotage."
  –Diane

"I just wanted to thank you for your book on sugar. You reached me down to my very soul. The footprints are clear on the long trail ahead of me, all I have to do is follow. "

    –Julie

"I am feeling inspired, even excited, about going off sugar. I don't feel deprived, but empowered, so thank you! I am going forward with the knowledge that it is definitely possible, and even highly desirable to quit!"

    –Lori

"Your book…changed my life. I've been battling my sugar addiction for 10 years and I loved the way you did it. I'm 32 and I'm sick of being sick of myself. Your book was just what I needed to read, the steps and suggestions are amazing and simple."

    –Krishna

"Your book has been very helpful in helping me kick the sugar habit for good, and is a wealth of information about how to sensibly [do this.] I'm now focusing on what I can eat, versus what I can't. I hope to be off the sugar rollercoaster, thanks in part to your book. "

    –Patricia

"As a sugar sensitive person and abstainer for a number of years now I feel as if you are writing about my own evolution of awareness. These are all of the steps, tips, mantras I've used over the years as I progressed to where I am today. Fit, lean & sugar-free. I've often been asked how I've done it and since you have written it down for me.I have learned not only how to care for myself through nutrition and fitness, but also I have learned just how good it feels to feel good about myself. You have done an excellent job communicating this process."

    –Angela G.

"Reading this book gave me a whole new perspective. I finally have come to a place of feeling like I don't want sugar- Yeah!!! Thank you so much for helping me make that connection."

    –Tiffany

"Reading your on-line book motivated me to return to a low-glycemic way of eating and also realize that I can't eat sugar – ever. With this new found motivation, I was finally to get back on track one month ago. I have lost weight and even more importantly, the depression I was experiencing while living on sugar has improved greatly. Thank you for your generosity and insight. Your sharing of your story has helped me realize that I can live without sugar and live well."

–Pam C.

"I have read your book so many times that I can practically quote from it. What never fails to inspire me is your personal story and all that you gave up when sugar was ruling your life. I always come away from it reminding myself that I simply cannot be the woman, wife, friend, employee that I want and deserve to be when sugar is in my daily life. I was not really able to put that concept into words until I read your book."

–Mary T.

"For many years, I have struggled with sugar addiction. Until recently, I did not know this problem was something that I shared with other people. Reading your book nightly is helping me to stay my course of healthy eating and abstinence from hidden and obvious sugars.

–Jen

"You've captured all my feelings, emotions and constant battles (within myself) for these last 3 years. Since banishing as much sugar as possible, five days ago, I've noticed I am a much calmer, focused and balanced individual in everyday life – What's more I no longer crave sugar and the daily constant yo-yo diets and self sabotage."

–Diane

"As soon as I read your book it hit me. I knew within five minutes that sugar was the issue. The relief I felt was overwhelming. I can solve this problem now that I know what it is. I can deal with withdrawal symptoms, etc. I just had no idea what it was I needed to avoid. You have opened the final door leading to my sanity."

–Chris

"Reading your story on your sugar addiction has opened my eyes completely. I suffer from binge eating and vomiting it up after and its always the sugar I crave. I'm not like everyone else, I can't eat sugar for a small treat then stop…it's like something in me just takes over….Thanks for sharing your story, it's helped me realize that sugar addiction is real and I'm going to try my best now to be free from this."

–*Bridget M.*

"Your book has been very helpful in helping me kick the sugar habit…and is a wealth of information about how to sensibly kick the sugar habit…I'm now focusing on what I can eat, versus what I can't. I hope to be off the sugar rollercoaster for good this time, thanks in part to your book."

–*Patricia B.*

OVERCOMING SUGAR ADDICTION:

How I Kicked My Sugar Habit and Created A Joyful Sugar Free Life

Karly Randolph Pitman

For more information please contact:

Five Oceans Press
P.O. Box 358
Livingston, MT 59047
E-mail: info@fiveoceanspress.com

ISBN: 9 781450 721912

Cover design: Brad Bunkers, Five Oceans Press
Interior design: Brad Bunkers, Five Oceans Press
Back cover photo: www.thomasleephoto.com

To Kathleen des Maisons,
who first taught me
about "sugar sensitivity"
and led me to freedom.

CONTENTS

1

Chapter One

WHY THIS BOOK?

When I began sharing my story of giving up sugar at FirstOurselves.org and other websites, I was flooded with questions from readers: How did you give up sugar? What do you eat? Can you help me give up sugar?

These questions made me realize that while there are many books available on why you should give up sugar, there aren't many books that teach you how to give up sugar. I know, firsthand, how painful sugar addiction can be. I also know how much freedom you gain when you release sugar's hold upon your life.

It is with this intention - to help you find that freedom, to release the painful effects of sugar addiction from your life - that I wrote this book.

I remember when I was pregnant for the first time, unsure of what the next nine months would bring. I picked up *What to Expect When You're Expecting* and used it as a guide to navigate the unfamiliar terrain of pregnancy. This book is written in that same spirit: to show you what to expect as you navigate a life without sugar.

Unlike pregnancy, giving up sugar is not perceived as a normal, common, everyday event. While more and more people are becoming cognizant of sugar's negative side effects, giving up sugar completely is the exception in our culture. You are a trailblazer, ahead of the curve. When you're at the forefront of a movement, it's greatly beneficial to have a hand to hold onto, someone who's gone before you, to help lead the way.

That's what I am offering.

I describe the peaks, the valleys, the good things, the bad things, the struggles, and the joys of giving up sugar for good. I'll offer tips to get you through sticky situations, like holidays or eating out in restaurants. I'll help you navigate the emotional terrain - because giving up sugar is about a lot more than just sugar.

If you find yourself feeling bogged down by too much information, if all the possible scenarios overwhelm you, remember that I'm sharing my experience. Your experience may be entirely different. As a newly pregnant mother, I found *What to Expect When You're Expecting* to be overwhelming at times, because it covered nearly every possible side effect of pregnancy. But as the months went by, I realized that not everything applied to me.

You'll probably find that to be true with my book, as well. Some of my tips will resonate with you and your experience; some won't. Use what works, and feel free to toss aside what doesn't.

I'm sure you'll come up with your own ideas on how to stay sugar free. We have women's forums on First Ourselves and a fan page on Facebook where you can share your story. We have much to learn from each other.

Introduction

The problem with sugar is not giving it up. I gave up sugar many times, went many days, weeks, and even months without eating sweets. My problem was giving it up for good. Is that your story? Do you go weeks without eating sugar, only to succumb to a plate of brownies, a cookie, a piece of birthday cake, or ice cream?

So how do you give up sugar - for good? How do you abstain from sugar for life? How do you find permanent freedom from the painful experience of sugar addiction?

That's what I'll show you in this book. I'll share what worked for me, tips and tricks that helped me find peace, and practical knowledge about how I live sugar free in a world that is saturated with sugar. And how I do it joyfully.

Before you dive in, I want to share what my book is not. My book is not meant to persuade you to give up your sugar habit. I won't have lists of the health ailments, problems, and negative side effects of eating sugar. My book is not filled with explanations of why, for many of us, sugar is one of the most addictive substances in the world. I don't explain the science of sugar addiction.

If you're looking for that information, I offer a reading list. There are several excellent books on the market that already cover this territory. My book is a companion to those guides, a supplement to the literature on sugar addiction. I would sample them all.

My book is not a persuasive tome on why you should give up sugar. If you're reading my book, I'm assuming that you're ready for action. You're aware of your sugar habit, you're ready for a change, and yet you're struggling with the follow through. That's how I can help.

My book is not a diet book, although kicking my sugar habit was one step in my getting off the diet-binge roller coaster. My book does not offer food lists, but I do share what I, personally eat. And yet I offer my story as an example, not a prescription.

Each person is different, and each person's sugar addiction is different. I, for example, am extremely "sugar sensitive". I also have low blood sugar. This means that in addition to abstaining from sugar in all of its forms, including honey, maple syrup, molasses, fruit sweetener, fructose, and brown rice syrup, I'm careful about monitoring my intake of foods with natural sugars like fruit, and simple carbohydrates that metabolically act like sugar in my body, namely flour and white rice.

But this may not be your story. You'll have to figure out for yourself if you need to just cut out sugar, or if popcorn triggers your sugar cravings, as well. As you will see in the following pages, my plan is to encourage you to learn to trust yourself: to listen to your body. To heed your intuition. To be a detective and a scientist: what happens when I eat ketchup? When I eat fruit? When I eat several servings of fruit? With trial and error, you will find which foods trigger your sugar cravings, and which do not.

So what can you expect to find in my book? A loving, supportive guide that gives you concrete, practical advice on joyfully navigating holidays, birthdays, and everyday in between sugar free.

This book is divided into several sections. In phase one, I'll lay a foundation and prepare you for your first few weeks without sugar, what I call sugar detox. In phase two, I'll help you through the detox phase. In phase three, I'll help you maintain your sugar abstinence for life. I also offer a suggested reading list, a food guide, and tips for holidays and other special occasions.

If I can give up sugar for good, anyone can. Take my hand, and dive in. What do you have to lose? Lots and lots of pain. What do you have to gain? Why, your very life.

A Word Of Caution

I'm not a nutritionist, doctor, nurse, medical professional, counselor, coach, or psychologist. I'm just a normal mom who kicked her sugar habit. The information I offer is for informational purposes only, and should not substitute for a doctor's care or advice. If you are concerned about the health implications of giving up sugar, or if you need medical advice, please talk to your doctor. My book is meant as a supplement to good medical and mental health care, not as a substitute for it.

If you experience any physical health problems, mental health problems, violent thoughts, suicidal thoughts, depression, or other drastic mood changes while eliminating sugar from your life, please see a doctor, a counselor, a psychologist, or a psychiatrist. Never struggle alone.

A Dedication To You, Dear Reader

And now, before we begin, I would like to offer you my deepest respect and admiration for the journey you are about to undertake. I commend your courage in facing your sugar addiction. I know how scary this is - giving up what feels like an old friend. I know you may be frightened, sad, or ambivalent: can I really do this?

I'm here to assure you that you can. I cheer your journey and believe in its fulfillment. You can do this.

To your health and wholeness,

Karly

2

MY STORY

I've been a sugar addict for most of my life. As a child, I ate sugar constantly, spending my allowance on candy and ice cream, baking cookies (and licking half the batter), and eating cupcakes, ice cream, and Pepsi on a daily basis. I didn't understand that once I began eating sugar, I couldn't stop. I would eat the entire bag of my Mom's candy, feeling ashamed by my behavior. I didn't mean to….it just happened.

I ate raw cookie dough, baked cupcakes, or had popcorn and Coke when I was feeling sad. As a teenager, I ran cross-country and track, so even though I was l eating a lot of sugar, I stayed thin. But my senior year in high school I began my first diet, which morphed into bulimia. I was bulimic for five years, during which time I consumed massive amounts of junk food: candy, cookies, bagels, brownies, pizza, tortilla chips, potato chips, ice cream, and Diet Coke.

At first, I was able to keep my weight down because I was throwing up so often. But the years of abuse took their toll, and the binging and purging and starving made my weight vacillate and my metabolism go haywire. I began gaining weight, which only fueled my desire to lose weight - and my binge/purge cycle.

In my 20s, I healed my bulimia, got married, and had my first child. I gave up my Diet Coke addiction because I was concerned about consuming aspartame while I was pregnant and breastfeeding. I was at my highest weight ever after giving birth to my first baby, which prompted me to read about nutrition and health. I read *Potatoes Not Prozac* and instantly recognized myself as a sugar addict. The information changed my life: finally, I understood why I could eat an entire bag of Twizzlers in one sitting.

Knowledge in hand, I attempted to cut back on my sugar consumption. I was a mother now, and I wanted to find a healthier way of eating, both for myself, and as an example for my family. I was running again, training for a marathon, and yet the baby weight wasn't coming off - odd considering how much I was exercising. I tried to make small, healthy changes: I swapped out candy for raisins, ate power bars and granola instead of cookies and ice cream, and used honey and fruit sweetener in my baking. I thought I was eating so much healthier because I was eating "natural" sugars.

But for my body, a sweet hit is a sweet hit, no matter whether it comes from a bag of Tootsie Rolls or a honey sweetened granola bar. I was still addicted to sugar, constantly craving something sweet. My moods were up and down; in fact, after we moved to Montana in 1998, they got terribly worse, and I battled an off and on depression for the next nine years.

I was lonely and isolated in a new town, living out in the country, and I didn't feel like running outside in the cold. My exercise faltered, my hormones went up and down through several more pregnancies, and life got incredibly stressful when my husband launched a business. I used food to comfort myself, baking cookies, making plates of nachos, eating half a pizza.

But as well as eating, I was also dieting, trying to lose the 15-20 pounds that cycled on and off my body with regularity. Whenever I wasn't pregnant, I was on a diet. That only led to the diet-binge roller coaster, where I'd be overeating one day, undereating the next. Most of the time, I ate healthfully. But then I would gorge myself on sugar, choosing "healthy" sugars like granola or raisins…or so I thought.

I kept reading about nutrition, sugar addiction, and depression. I knew that my sugar addiction was a huge part of my problem, and garnered the courage to try and live sugar free. But every time I gave up sugar, I'd feel deprived. I'd be sugar free for months, and would feel fantastic.

And then…

I would have a piece of cake, justifying my indulgence by vowing to return to my sugar abstinence the next day. I would tell myself I would eat just one serving and put the rest away, forgetting that I have never been able to eat just one piece of cake my entire life. One cookie would turn to two, then three; to candy the next day; brownies thereafter, then an entire can of raisins. Before I knew it, I was bingeing on sugar, eating out of control, riding an emotional roller coaster of mood swings, depression, and irritability.

Finally, I would reach a point of self-disgust, and give up sugar again. Then the cycle would start anew….staying off sugar for months, only to give in and eat sugar, then going off sugar, then eating sugar again. This painful cycle went on for nearly a decade. I went off and on sugar more times than I care to count. I wore six different sizes, a consequence of how much I was bingeing. But in the beginning of 2007, after one too many sugar binges, I embraced a new truth about myself: I can't eat sugar. Ever. I'll be sugar free for the rest of my life.

I didn't want to accept this. I still secretly wanted to eat sugar, just without the negative side effects. The prospect of never eating apple pie or a chocolate chip cookie again was so heartbreaking that I couldn't stay the course. But I had to accept my truth: that my body doesn't react normally to sugar. I can't eat a sugary treat, every now and then, without leading to a binge. I had to get to the point that my sugar binges were making me so miserable that the alternative, abstinence, looked appealing.

What Woke Me Up

My rock bottom moment came down to this: I can't live the life I want to live if I'm bingeing on sugar. I can't be the parent (my children will glee-fully relay that sugar turns me into Witch Mommy), wife (nothing like a gassy stomach to make you feel sexy!), woman (it's really hard to feel good about your body when you feel sick and bloated from overeating), writer, or friend that I want to be while I'm depressed, eating sugar out of control. I was either bingeing on sugar or recovering from my food "hangovers," isolating myself, hanging out in my basement. Either way, I wasn't present. I was stuck.

It became a question of sugar - or my life.

I chose my life.

It was an easy decision. Easy in that I knew that I wanted to live. And yet its daily implementation means giving myself excellent self care, support, and nurturing. It means working hard at caring for myself, and sometimes I do get tired of this. Sometimes I wish I didn't have to be so aware all the time.

Choosing my health over sugar means being willing to live differently than the vast majority of other people. It means saying no to things I'd like to say yes to: birthday cake, Christmas baking, and apple pie. Making peace with these trade-offs was one of the keys to my giving up sugar.

When I don't eat sugar, I feel fantastic: my moods, blood sugar, and emotions are stable. I don't suffer from physical cravings. My self esteem rises. My health improves. My weight is more stable.

The physical cravings for sugar disappeared rather quickly. But the emotional cravings? Those reappear. That was the deeper work I embraced after I physically detached from sugar.

And yet I stay the course, even though, at times, it's hard. What's harder is bingeing on food instead of snuggling with my kids; tiptoeing in the kitchen for snacks instead of connecting with my husband; hiding myself from the world because I'm bloated and depressed. That is hard.

Abstaining from sugar doesn't deprive my spirit. Avoiding my life - or wishing it away - because I'm sugar addicted, does.

3

GETTING READY FOR SUGAR DETOX

How you decide to give up sugar is up to you. You may give yourself several months to gradually wean yourself from sugar. Or, you may go the cold turkey route, where you give up all forms of sugar at once. I would suggest giving yourself time to create some foundation behaviors - what I call Grounding - before you throw yourself into sugar abstinence. Grounding can affect how easy or difficult this process is for you.

No matter which route you choose - all at once, or slow and steady - at some point, you'll sit with your desire to eat sugar and say no. That first week without any sugar poses its challenges. I want you to feel up to the challenge. So before we do anything, before we subtract sugar from your life, we're going to add things to your life. We're going to bolster your courage, ground you in good habits and pave the way to make the challenge ahead as easy as possible. Before you give up sugar, I suggest spending a few weeks - or months if it takes that long; and it often does - implementing the following changes, so you have a strong base for the journey ahead.

Preparing Your Body

Eat breakfast every day. Breakfast sets the foundation for your whole day. If I had to pick one habit out of all of the many that have helped me remain sugar free, I would say eating breakfast is the biggest key to my success.

You can't resist sugar's siren pull if you're hungry. Period. So be kind to yourself: eat breakfast. Stabilize your blood sugar. Pick something sugar free, with some protein - it doesn't even have to be a typical breakfast food. Eat enough so that you're satisfied, but not overstuffed. Some of my favorite breakfasts are salmon and vegetables, or an egg frittata with lots and lots of vegetables. I enjoy crustless quiches, giant salads with black beans or grilled chicken, lentil soup, chili, and plain kefir (it's like yogurt) with almonds, flaxseed, and walnuts.

When I have a filling breakfast, my whole day goes better. My moods are more stable. I eat less throughout the day. I feel better. I'm a more patient mother. My desire for junk food lessens. And I'm usually full for a good three to four hours.

Contrast this experience with when I skipped breakfast. I used to play this weird food game, where I'd try and wait as long as possible in the day before eating. I thought it would help me lose weight - I was always heavier than I wanted to be as a consequence of my sugar binges - but it backfired. Instead, I'd find that I was hungrier for skipping breakfast, and more than made up for it in the evening with a huge binge.

Eat regularly. Eating regularly keeps your moods and blood sugar stable, keeping you from becoming overhungry. When you're overhungry, you usually overeat at the next meal, or give in to a quick sugar hit. This is where prevention - eating regularly - is better than suffering the aftermath of a sugar binge.

I eat every 3 to 4 hours throughout the day. I find that becoming too hungry is overarousing. I get almost panicky about food, irritable and light headed (common for those with low blood sugar.) I'm also sensitive, and when you're sensitive, hunger can feel super intense. Most people who are sensitive to sugar are sensitive period. Nourishing your body on a regular basis, giving yourself a consistent rhythm, feels predictable, regular and safe.

Structure is very grounding for those of us who are sugar sensitive - and we're the ones who most often resist it. I try not to judge my resistance to structure but observe it with openness and wonder. "What's really here?" I often ask myself. I find that underneath the resistance are often feelings, like fear (fear of failing, fear of being "flawed" or broken, fear that I'll never change), sadness, or anger.

Turn towards your resistance and embrace its message. Ask it point black, "Why are you afraid?" This is always an interesting exercise for me.

Listening to my feelings is what softens my resistance to caring for myself. I realize, "Oh, I'm just tired from cooking for myself all the time," or, "I get irritated sometimes that I'm so high maintenance - or that I feel like I'm high maintenance." I care for my feelings and they soften. They open up and allow me to cook the meal, especially when I don't feel like it.

Trying to undereat throughout the day backfires. It sets you up for sugar cravings. I guarantee it. Pay particular attention to the afternoon, the 3 p.m. window. I make myself a hearty snack at this time every day, as I'm usually very hungry at this time. When I skip my afternoon snack, I often overeat at dinner, because I've waited too long to eat, and I'm overhungry.

Eat protein at every meal. I have some protein at every meal, such as nuts, meat, dairy, or legumes. Protein helps stabilize my blood sugar and keeps my energy constant. You don't have, or want to, overeat protein. I try to eat 15-25 grams of protein at every meal. This is enough to keep me full for a few hours, but not so much that I feel heavy and sluggish. You may need more or less depending on your body size and activity level.

Eat more fibrous carbohydrates. Except for fiber, all carbohydrates are eventually broken down into sugar in the body. This is why your body can react to a plate of mashed potatoes in the same way it reacts to a candy bar: they are both metabolically treated as sugar.

That being said, some carbs are broken down into sugar more quickly than others. Foods that are broken down slowly are foods that are low on the gylcemic index. Foods that are broken down quickly into sugar are high on the gylcemic index. (Go to www.glycemicindex.com for more information on the gylcemic index, as well as a database for finding out the glycemic index of foods.)

For now, focus on eating complex carbohydrates, foods that break down slowly. Choose lots and lots of non-starchy vegetables like salad greens, leafy greens (kale and spinach, for example), green beans, onions, mushrooms, bell peppers, etc. Eat whole grains versus processed grains. Try brown rice, barley, millet, quinoa, or steel cut oats. Eat low sugar fruits, like berries and apples, instead of high sugar fruits, like dried fruits, pineapple, and grapes. Starchy carbohydrates like yams, red potatoes and winter squash and legumes (black beans, pinto beans, chickpeas, lentils, and more) are also complex carbohydrates you can enjoy.

Eat enough to be full. Sometimes our bodies crave sugar because they're underfed. This can especially be true if you've been chronically undereating or dieting. As Julia Ross points out in her excellent book, *The Diet Cure,* consuming too few calories and nutrients sets your body up for sugar cravings and a terrible mood. This was true in my life. When I was in college, I tried to eat as little as possible and be as thin as possible, so I was constantly starving. Is it any wonder that once I gave myself permission to eat, I consumed massive amounts of candy, white flour and sugary desserts?

In my 20s, I was on a chronic diet. My pattern of eating was to eat as little as I could throughout the day, only to be starving by dinnertime. Then I would eat the equivalent of three dinners because I was so hungry, going to bed with a stomachache.

My advice? Eat enough throughout the day so that you're satisfied. I've found that eating a good sized breakfast and lunch of protein, some fat, non-starchy vegetables and some slow carbs (like hummus or lentils) keeps me feeling good throughout the day, and binge free at dinner.

Eat your meals sitting down, on a plate. Do you tend to eat your meals on the run, standing up, in the kitchen? Particularly if you're a mom, you may squeeze your meals in between errands and a neverending to-do list. You are worth 25 minutes to sit down, put your meal on a plate, and enjoy your food. When you stand up and eat out of the container, the pot, or the bag, you'll eat more than you realize. This is mindless eating; how you eat an entire bag of potato chips in one sitting.

You also won't taste or enjoy your food. Your stomach may be full but your heart is empty. When we're absent from our eating, our "emotional" stomach isn't satisfied. We look for more food to fill the void.

Add exercise. Historically, I loved being active. I was a runner, liked working out at the gym and lifting weights, and enjoyed an active yoga practice.

As I've gotten older, I've grown much softer towards myself overall, and this includes pushing myself so hard with exercise. I look back and see how much of my exercise striving was based on a feeling of lack - how much I wanted to feel strong, in charge and "good enough." I was always in competition to be the best version of myself. I also liked to exercise to "make up" for overeating. So the more pain the better.

Today, I approach exercise from a space of enjoyment - to enjoy moving my body and caring for myself. I don't exercise as punishment or in an effort to control my body or weight - although that voice of, "I should be 10 pounds thinner!" can pop up in my head, too.

With this different approach, I take a lot more walks, hikes, do more yoga and feel less of a need to push. I let myself go dancing - something I love - versus slaving away at a gym class I can't stand. I also find that I'm much less resistant to exercise. I'm more consistent.

Before you embark on your sugar detox, I'd encourage you to add some gentle exercise. This doesn't have to be a hard core, boot camp type program

- in fact, I would suggest not doing anything super intense. Going off sugar is intense enough on its own. Focusing on one goal at a time is being kind to yourself by accepting your limits. You are not superhuman; nor should you try to be.

Exercise can be as simple as a daily walk, a swim a few times a week, or a bike ride. If you already have an exercise routine, try to keep it consistent.

This step is important because going off sugar is a huge change. Exercise can be an anchor that helps you feel more grounded during a time when everything feels different, unfamiliar and uncomfortable.

If you've used sugar for comfort, you'll be without your crutch. You may confront all sorts of painful feelings and beliefs that you used to stuff with ice cream. Those feelings will need an outlet, and exercise is a wonderful escape.

So go for a walk. I know I always feel better, and my problems more sur-mountable, when I'm out in the open air, away from the confines of home. If it's blistering cold outside, do a ten minute strength training routine of some push-ups, crunches, stretches, or simple yoga poses. Use your Netflix subscription and rent some fitness DVDs. Go on bike rides. Walk the dog. Just do *something*. If you've been living in a sugar fog, you may feel sepa-rated from your body. Exercise can help you reestablish that connection, to remember how good it feels to move, to feel strong, to feel healthy and alive. It will motivate you to make good choices, to choose an apple over apple pie; almonds over an almond joy.

Eat sugar with a meal. If you're going to eat sugar, eat it with a meal, with some protein. This will minimize sugar's negative effect on your blood sugar. Even though adding protein won't change sugar's effect on your endorphins and your appetite, this is a good start until you're prepared to relinquish sugar for good.

Preparing Your Mind

Track your patterns. Why do you succumb to sugar? When? What types of sugary foods do you eat? What emotional triggers cause you to crave sugar? These are all questions that you can answer by keeping a food diary. It offers you clues to help you figure out what foods trigger sugar cravings, which foods don't; which foods make you feel good; which foods make you feel lousy.

When you keep a food diary, track these things: what you eat, how you feel, when you experience cravings, and when you're hungry. Does your energy fluctuate? What about your moods? As this information accumulates over the weeks, you'll be able to locate the patterns in your eating, as well as the connection between foods and your mood.

Maybe you'll learn that eating a fruit smoothie and a bowl of corn flakes for breakfast sets you up for sugar cravings, whereas an omelet and turkey sausages keeps you satisfied and crave-free. You can also find ties to emotional triggers - does anxiety feed your sugar cravings? What about stress? How about an argument with a loved one, or times of sadness? With this knowledge, you'll be able to plan in advance for these circumstances, to find a sugar free substitute for handling these emotions. The key is preparation: to have an alternative plan in place before these situations occur.

Focus on healing. You can use positive affirmations, inspiring quotes, and inspiring literature to keep your mind trained on your goal. Focus on where you want to go; not where you've been.

Here are some of my favorite health related affirmations:

I choose healthy foods that nourish my body.

I am an excellent caretaker of my body.

I honor my body with healthy foods.

I love and accept myself.

I enjoy my health.

I celebrate all the wonderful foods that I can eat.

I nourish myself everyday.

I am so proud of myself.

Fill your mind with beautiful words. Inspiring books and literature can be a great source of peace and calm. I also love poetry for its soothing qualities. Mary Oliver, Rumi, Hafiz, and Rilke are some of my favorite poets.

You may want to consider limiting your intake of negative media, news, and movies. One of my favorite ways of encouraging myself is by watching inspiring sports movies. These "believe in your dreams" movies serve as powerful metaphors for life. My favorites include: *Hoosiers, Rudy, The Rookie, The Greatest Game Ever Played, Believe in Me, Invincible, Miracle, Dreamer, Glory Road, Remember the Titans,* and *Akeelah and the Bee.*

Create positive mental pictures and visualize your success. We all have mental pictures - ways that we picture ourselves, and what we believe about ourselves in our minds. These mental pictures have an incredible influence on our behavior.

Meditation teacher Tara Brach says that we can all get caught in the "small self." This is where we start to think that we are our bingeing, our overeating, our pain, our problems. Then we get caught in this "trance" where we act out this small self with the pain, bingeing and overeating.

You'll be undergoing huge changes when you give up sugar. It's important that your mental pictures adapt to the new you, that you find ways to unhook from this small self. If you think of yourself as an overweight sugar addict, you'll find it easy to act like an overweight sugar addict.

While you work on changing your habits, see yourself as a sugar free person. See yourself as someone who makes healthy food choices, who exercises, who takes excellent care of themselves.

One of the easiest ways to create a new mental image is to make a dreamboard, a photo collage of images that speak to you. Gather pictures, words, magazine clippings, and poems, anything that makes your spirit sing. Make a collage of your ideal physical self. Cut out photos of delicious meals that are sugar free. Create visual pictures of what freedom from sugar will look like for you, whether it's wearing a bathing suit for the first time in years, or having the courage to write your novel, or being a more patient parent.

You can also use positive mental pictures as ways of ingraining new habits. Do you graze the kitchen after dinner, eating sweet after sweet? Start rehearsing a new script in your mind: picture yourself having the sugar cravings, really feel yourself having the urge to eat sugar. But, instead of giving into your cravings, visualize yourself getting up, brushing your teeth, reading a book, and taking deep breaths. Picture your success, and rehearse it often. This helps cement new behavior patterns.

I found meditation and mindfulness practices very helpful in unhooking from the "small self." Sitting with my feelings instead of running from them - looking at my patterns with compassion and awareness - helped me quiet the drive for food. It fostered forgiveness for myself, softening the voice of judgment.

Write your food history. You may find it helpful to do as I did and write your food history. I wrote about my weight, my health, and my relationship with food, starting at childhood and moving to the present day.

Looking at my food history in this way gave me a bird's eye view: What patterns did I see? Any similarities? Differences? What foods did I binge on throughout my life? What foods did I use for comfort? How did I treat food differently in the summer, versus the winter? How did food affect my mood, my health, and my weight?

This information can be incredibly valuable, especially as you ponder the decision to give up sugar. For example, there was a time when I questioned my sugar sensitivity at all, thinking that I overate sugar because I didn't allow myself to eat it. It was my labeling of sugar as bad that fed the anxiety that caused me to overeat it.

I loved this idea of giving myself permission to eat whatever I wanted, to not label certain foods as "bad." So I decided to try it, and see if I could eat sugar in moderation. Needless to say, this experiment was a grand failure. I was craving and overeating sugar around the clock.

This is where my food history came in handy. As I surveyed my life, I was able to find (and face) the evidence that I haven't been able to eat sugar moderately, ever. Even as a child, before I knew about sugar addiction, I abused it. With this knowledge, I could recognize that abstaining from sugar wasn't about labeling it as "good" or "bad" but appreciating how it was "bad" - bad in the sense that it felt terrible in my body - for me.

Flip the switch. Do you really want to give up sugar for good? I ask you this question, because for years, while I *said* I wanted to give up sugar, deep down, I really didn't want to. I was lying. What I wanted was to be thin and healthy and stop overeating....and still be able to eat sugar.

I didn't want to choose. I didn't want to accept life's limits. I didn't want to accept the pain and loss of eliminating sugar.

I'm not able to have health, weight loss, and normalized eating...and still eat sugar. It took me years to come to that point of understanding and acceptance, but once I did, giving up sugar was much easier. I call it flipping the switch: I finally made the choice. I finally accepted what I couldn't change - that sugar makes me crazy - and accepted the consequences of this limit - staying off sugar.

With this deep rooted acceptance, I approached sugar abstinence with my whole heart, instead of with solely will power, drive and discipline. There was more of "me" present with my choice, willing to do the work of saying no. I wasn't fighting so much internally about "I wish I could" versus "I shouldn't."

We all say we want the same things: "I want to have more money. I want to be healthier. I want to lose weight. I want to give up sugar. I want to be less stressed."

These are merely wishful thinking as long as we're overspending, eating junk, eating sugar, and overscheduling our lives. How do we know when we really want to change?

When we act. When we go out for a walk, implement a budget, change our eating habits, and take time to relax.

How will you know when you're ready to give up sugar? When *you're* ready to put away the brownies, and create a lifestyle of new habits.

Preparing Your Spirit

Mourn sugar's loss in your life. When I gave up sugar for good, I spent several weeks mourning sugar's loss. It may sound a bit melodramatic, but I cried for the loss of my friend. I grieved over the fact that I won't taste my grandma's apple pie, ice cream on a hot summer day, or sugar cookies shaped like candy canes and reindeer on the holidays.

We have to let go of the old, in order to make way for the new. We can't hold onto our desire for sugar while releasing sugar's hold on our lives. Something has to give. Something has to go.

The first part of letting go is acceptance. In his work, psychologist Gordon Neufeld speaks about the importance of reaching "the wall of futility." Your "wall of futility" is when you accept that, yes, while you would like to eat sugar; no, you're not able to eat it and maintain excellent health at the same time. You accept the futility, your lack of control over the situation. You accept what you can't change.

Accepting futility lays the groundwork for the next step: mourning your losses. It's okay to be sad about not eating sugar. After all, sugar has probably paid a huge part in your life. Let yourself grieve what you can't change.

Only after you've accepted and mourned your losses are you able to move forward. Now you can take the necessary steps to plan for a life without sugar. Now you can build a strong foundation. Now you can think of ways to add joy, comfort, celebration and care in your life without sweet treats.

Tend your sadness as well as your happiness. Release your grief, those burdens of the soul. It is rich compost for a fertile garden: the blossoming thing that is your sugar free life.

As grief and mourning reappear - which they will - cry your tears. Name your feelings - loss, sadness, grief, anger, frustration. Name them and put your hand on your heart and tell yourself, "I care about this suffering." Say, "I care about this sadness." Your care softens your feelings. It's not much different than a child who feels inside out and who softens when you hold him on your lap.

You will grieve over and over again throughout your journey. Life is full of many losses, both big and small. We often minimize our losses, particularly losses that our minds say "aren't important" like sadness over a cupcake.

Minimizing our pain doesn't make it go away. It eventually turns into resentment and self sabotage. Turning towards our pain and caring for it is what keeps us from repressing and then acting out in a binge.

Find the gift in sugar addiction. We all have "stuff" - the lessons and stumbling blocks that reoccur throughout our lives. If you're reading this book, abusing sugar may be some of your "stuff." If you're like me, you may have spent considerable energy burying this stuff. You may have avoided it. You may have denied it. You may have compared your stuff to other people's stuff - I'm not as bad as her. Anything to keep you from facing your stuff.

You may compare your stuff to other people's stuff and feel like you're the worst human being, ever. You may feel broken, flawed, helpless, hopeless. You may look at your sugar addiction and all your food pain and feel disgust, self-loathing and shame.

We all have pain. Rain falls on us all, as we also all get our share of joy. It's not personal. This is the hardest thing for so many of us to see. We think the pain is our fault. We think, "If only...." If only I would have been more nurtured as a kid, if only I wouldn't have started that first diet, if only I would've exercised more, if I only I weren't depressed.... If only I could've prevented all this pain.

I would love to hold you in my arms and reassure you that it's not your fault. It's not some curse from the universe that you're sensitive to sugar. God isn't out to get you. You didn't do anything wrong to deserve this. It's not a punishment.

The ancient Greeks believed that our afflictions were gifts from the Gods. They aren't meant to punish but to help us see - what needs healing? Where am I off balance? What is arising in me? What is calling for attention?

Your sugar sensitivity is merely a part of you asking for your attention, care and love. There are many rewards to honoring our sugar sensitivity, of learning how to care for ourselves without sweets. These include finding an inner sanctuary, gaining inner wisdom, trust and clarity, and finding gentleness and compassion for ourselves as we stop trying to push ourselves so hard. Who knows if we would find these things without this journey out of sugar?

We are such tender creatures in need of greater mercy and lovingkindness. Recognize your struggles as a gift to open you to this love and tenderness.

Embrace the journey as something valuable and necessary, as something with intertwined gifts of discovery.

See yourself as whole. I came across a quote that I love: "May I accept all aspects of my being and see them as holy." I think it's important to embrace this perspective, otherwise, it's easy to get bogged down in an, "I'm a worthless addict" mentality.

While you may have addictive or painful patterns with food, this is not the sum of who you are. It doesn't define you. This is the "small self," the limited thinking that Tara Brach describes in her work. It's a sign that we're judging ourselves harshly, and judging our worth as human beings based on our behavior instead of our inherent dignity.

We don't like unhooking from the "small self" because we think that it's a form of denial. We think that if we cut ourselves some slack we'll be out of control.

The reverse is what is true - and how we heal. When we can look at ourselves with awareness - unfliching, with complete honesty and presence - we can see that even our "bad" habits are an attempt to care for ourselves. We can see the holiness in our flaws. It may not be pretty, but the roots of our behavior are kind. By trusting our goodness in this way, we can change our habits to ones that don't cause us suffering. We don't feel as bogged down by guilt and self-loathing.

Instead of calling you - or me - a sugar addict, I prefer to use Kathleen des Maisons' term, sugar sensitive. It may feel like semantics, but I feel it's the difference between defining ourselves by our behavior versus recognizing our many different selves.

See all aspects of your being as holy. See your body, even with its sugar sensitivity, as something good. Instead of focusing on your frailties, focus on your health, wholeness, and inner goodness.

Focusing on your holiness is how you heal your sugar addiction; not by pummeling yourself with criticism about what a terrible sugar addict you are.

Add self care. As you eliminate sugar from your life, you'll create a vacuum, an empty space once filled with trips to Dairy Queen, barbeques with ice cream, and Christmas baking with your family. If you used sugar for comfort or care, you need to find a way to meet those needs without sugar. Otherwise, you'll feel neglected, malnourished and anxious.

This can lead to overeating any food even after you've stopped eating sugar. You're looking for a food fix - external soothing - because you haven't gained skills in internal soothing.

Many of us who turn to sugar for comfort never learned how to soothe ourselves without food. This is understandable - it's not taught in our culture, and many of us had families who weren't able to give us this kind of nurturing.

It helps to think of non-food soothing activities you can do to comfort yourself. If you're feeling stuck, think back to what you did as a child. Children are naturals at self soothing. Did you listen to music, sing, ride your bike, jump rope, draw, color, take a nap, cuddle with a stuffed animal, take a bath, play in the sprinkler, rock in a rocking chair, care for a baby doll or teddy bear, play tag, wrestle or do some other rough play, cook, play with a sibling or friend, climb a tree, make a fort, or go off by yourself?

Spend some time writing in your journal and explore your soothing rituals. Most adults have soothing rituals that revolve around TV, food, drink and shopping. Many of us have lost touch with the inner child who has much simpler - and often wiser - ways of soothing ourselves.

Can you add some of these activities back into your life? If you liked to draw as a child, can you spend some time in the evening doing some kind of art or other creative activity? Can you go for a bike ride, a drive in the car while singing to your favorite music, or take a walk?

One of the reasons why we resist giving up sugar is that we think it will mean the end of soothing and comfort. The problem is not sugar but that our definition of care is so small, and so focused on food. There are a million ways to give yourself the real nurturing you so desire. The key is giving yourself permission. It's easy and costs little to grab a candy bar for a pick me up. It feels much more selfish somehow to take an hour for our care and nourishment.

I like to give myself a small monthly allowance of $20 that is my pamper fund. I use it to buy myself gourmet teas, art supplies, a book of poetry or a novel, a crossword puzzle book, jewelry making supplies, knitting supplies, or beauty products. You may use your monthly allowance to buy something altogether different. The key is using this money for your pleasure.

Self care works best when it's a regular practice. Give yourself 20 or 30 minutes of alone time everyday when you can read, do something physical, call a friend, create something with your hands, or take a hot bath. I like to give myself a gift of the first 30 minutes of my day. That's when I do some journaling, read, meditate, and let myself gently begin the tasks of the day.

Work on cultivating your self-care before you tackle your sugar detox, so that it's a regular practice. By doing so, you're coming from a place of nurturance - versus deprivation - when you remove sugar.

Make peace with your biochemistry. There are times when I've been so frustrated with my body's biochemistry that I feel hopeless. It feels too hard and like it's too much work. I want to throw in the towel, say, "What the hell!" and binge on sugar.

It's important to make peace with our unique body chemistry. A huge part of healing my desire for sugar was this vital step: acceptance. For a long time, I denied, ignored, and rallied against my sugar addiction. I didn't want to accept that I'm "sugar sensitive." This denial kept me in limbo land, volleying back and forth between sugar abstinence one week, and sugar bingeing the next. I couldn't let it go, this desire for sugar.

It's the same attitude that precluded me from accepting other aspects of my personality: my sensitivity, my tenderheartedness, and my tendency to become overwhelmed by stress. For years, I've tried to be someone else; to be less emotional, less fearful; more strong, less sensitive. But those things are what make me, me. While I can grow and change and work on my stumbling blocks, it doesn't change the beautiful perfection of my divine creation. Do you believe you were created in the image of God? Or do you see your faults as evidence of a cosmic mistake?

I read this statement in *Eat, Pray, Love* recently: "God dwells within you, as you." Your "sugar sensitivity" is God, just as your talents are God, just as your kindness is God, just as your love is God.

There's nothing wrong with being "sugar sensitive." It's not a character fault. It's not a deficiency. It's not a punishment. It's not proof that there's something wrong about you. It just *is*. Viewed from this lens, caring for your "sugar sensitivity" just *is*, too - the natural consequence of acceptance, a heartfelt expression of appropriate care and wisdom - not something to punish you or hurt you or that's proof of your "weakness."

Your challenges with sugar can be a gift to grow your compassion, your discipline, your presence, your mercy. If you turn towards it and embrace it, softening the subtle judgment of, "I'm not okay. I'm broken. I'm bad," sugar sensitivity can be your greatest teacher.

Man your support team. You can't give up sugar by yourself. You will need a support team. But this is tricky, because giving up sugar isn't always recognized as something positive. Sugar is ingrained into every aspect of our society. It's a socially acceptable addiction. So if you ask your husband or sister for support in giving up sugar, they may think you're joking. They may tell you you're being too strict. They probably love you and care about you but don't understand how much of a problem sugar is for you.

I hear from plenty of people who are sugar sensitive and who have spouses or partners who are not. And while their partners may not understand, they are supportive. So on the one hand, don't underestimate the support you can get from others even if they don't personally suffer from a sugar sensitivity.

If you find that people in your life genuinely aren't supportive, keep asking for help until you do find it. Maybe you won't be able to lean on your sister, but you have a good friend who will cheer you on. Maybe you'll need to hire a counselor to support yourself. Maybe you'll need to rely on a pastor, an online support forum, or a local support group. If you have children, and they're old enough to understand, enlist their help. My children were thrilled to be my "allies."

Find spiritual solace. I'm a spiritual person, and I like to pray, meditate, and connect with the Divine. While not everyone shares my spiritual beliefs, and I certainly don't expect you to, I encourage you to find spiritual solace in whatever feeds your connection with Spirit. Pray to God, ask for help, do yoga, chant, call on angels, meditate, read religious literature, go out in nature, attend a Bible study, build an altar, perform a ritual, make art, recite a mantra: do whatever fortifies your spiritual core. The truth is, you don't have to do this alone. There are untold resources, both seen, and unseen, that are waiting to come to your aid.

I found that connecting my journey out of sugar to something greater than myself gave me the strength - and purpose - to keep going when it felt very hard. For many years, not eating sugar was a form of spiritual practice for me. I did it as an act of service, because I knew I couldn't offer the world my love, attention and care when I was fixated on sugar. Holding that larger perspective greatly helped me when I was in pain.

Today, my sugar abstinence is more in the background, something I don't have to focus on with as much discipline. That's probably because there are now other areas in my life where I get hooked and get to practice! For example, after I worked on my sugar stuff I found I had a giant knot of deeper food issues to untangle. Life is a constant teacher. And yet going through the unraveling process with sugar gave me the courage to face my stuff with food. With sugar, I learned that I could continue to walk my path, even when the going was tough, I got mud all over my face, and I stumbled over and over again. This carries over into other areas of growth and challenge.

Envision where you want to be. Stay focused on the end goal. While you're in the midst of sugar detox, you may want to quit, give up, or decide that sugar abstinence is impossible. Plan ahead for these occasions: where do you want to be in a year? In five? What do you want to look like? Do you want to be thinner, or in better shape? What kind of health do you want? Are there dreams or goals that you'd like to accomplish? Have you put off things because you've been too bogged down by your sugar addiction? Imagine yourself accomplishing them. Hold onto this vision in the coming months. The best advice for when it hurts? "This, too, shall pass." Nothing is forever.

Preparing Your Home And Loved Ones

Prepare your family. Let your loved ones know what to expect, as we all get nervous around change. After all, if you're making drastic changes to your diet, they might be concerned: Does this mean we'll never have cookies or ice cream again? They want to know how your food choices will impact them, what you need from them, and what to expect.

Explain that you're giving up sugar. Explain that this is not a diet…that this is a lifetime commitment. Explain that, yes, initially, you'll need to limit your exposure to sweets and goodies, and ask for their cooperation so that you don't feel tempted to eat sugar. But also tell them that after the first week or two, you should be free of any sugar cravings. Over time, you will be able to have sugar in the house again without feeling tempted to eat it.

Explain *exactly* how they can help you. People love hearing how they can help because we often don't know and then do nothing in our clumsiness. Give them very specific ways they can support you, as in eating candy at the office instead of at home, or going for a walk with you after dinner when you're feeling tempted to eat dessert.

Prepare them for how you may feel those first 10 days without sugar. Explain that you may be tired, irritable, or up and down: let them know that this has nothing to do with them, but is a consequence of giving up sugar. Reassure them that your sugar detox is about you, not them, so they don't feel as if their food choices are threatened. This is especially important with spouses: you don't want your partner to feel as if you're attacking his or her food choices by your decision to give up sugar in your own life.

Prepare your kitchen. Giving up sugar may mean cooking different foods, or eating things you aren't used to cooking. Give yourself time to learn about different foods and to stock your kitchen. If you have your family's support, begin eliminating sugary foods from the home. Stop buying sodas, keeping candy, ice cream, and cookies around the house; substitute healthier foods for sugary treats (oatmeal instead of sugary cereals; string cheese instead of sweetened yogurts; almonds and cashews instead of potato chips.)

If they're resistant to giving up their treats, see if they'd be willing to go out for ice cream, for example, instead of eating it at home. Or see if they will do as my family did: when I was detoxing from sugar, I asked them to hide my favorite sweet treats, like granola, until I had more willpower. My children thought this was way too much fun. They also hid it *very* well, because I went looking. More than once.

Search the internet for low sugar recipes, and come up with a basic repertoire of quick, easy, low sugar meals and snacks, such as a roast chicken, brown rice, and steamed broccoli; scrambled eggs and turkey sausage; plain yogurt with chopped almonds and berries. Stock your home with foods that you can eat while you're quitting sugar, so you aren't tempted to reach for sugar just because you're hungry, and your home is absent of healthy foods.

Some things that I always have in my house include: a variety of raw nuts, such as cashews, walnuts, pecans and almonds (I keep mine in the fridge to keep them from going rancid.) String cheese, plain yogurt and kefir, hummus dip (Costco sells a great one that is sugar free), black beans, pinto beans, and 10 bean soup mix.

I try to keep apples and berries in the house (I buy frozen in the winter, fresh in the summer.) Standard veggies like carrots, celery, broccoli and red bell peppers are usually in the fridge, along with makings for a salad. My freezer has small packs of wild Alaskan salmon, quick to defrost for easy meals, a variety of meats, such as whole chickens (for roasting and soups), chicken thighs, venison, and bison. I also keep a variety of frozen vegetables on hand.

I buy dry legumes in bulk - black beans, lentils, pinto beans, split peas, a 10 bean soup mix, chickpeas - so my pantry is always full, but I also buy a few cans of beans to keep on hand when I don't have time to soak and cook beans from scratch.

Create a supportive environment. Aside from your kitchen, think about how you can create a supportive environment in other areas of your home. Minimize triggers: those things that spark your sugar cravings. Triggers are overarousing and cause anxiety. We see the treat and immediately we want to act on that impulse and eat it. So changing that pattern - *not* acting on the impulse and not eating the treat - is exhausting. It's hard work! It can create anxiety as we try and avoid situations where we're hooked into wanting sugar and consciously trying to say no. Then - and this is where it gets really interesting - we want to eat to soothe this anxiety, our fears about avoiding temptation. So we're doubly hooked by food.

In the beginning stages of going off sugar, it can be a kindness to yourself to minimize these situations where you're hooked. It gives you a greater chance of success because you aren't exhausted and overaroused from trying to be "good" all the time. (Later on down the road, you treat these situations differently - you don't need as many boundaries or controls because you have more separation from the pattern of brownie-I want to eat it. I cover more of this in chapter 5.)

Do you have to have a coke or a candy when you go to the movies? If you feel like you won't be able to avoid temptation, then it may be best to stay away from the movies for a while, or to go with a friend who can support you in staying away from the candy counter. If going out to dinner means dessert, then eat at home for a few weeks.

I know this step can feel like deprivation, like you're eliminating things from your life. But it's only for a time. That's why it's also important to remember to balance removing things from your life with adding things to your life - the self care component I talked about earlier. Look at eliminating your triggers as supporting yourself, not depriving yourself. There's nothing more discouraging

than attempting to give up sugar and finding yourself unsuccessful, time and time again. Be kind to yourself by not making this step any harder than it needs to be.

Remember that sugar is about you, not your family or friends. In your enthusiasm, you may want to have your friends and family join you in your quest. But the other people in your life may not be at a similar place of decision.

Don't feel like you have to convert your friends and family to your way of living. You are choosing to give up sugar...for you. That's enough. If your loved ones sense that you're judging them for their eating habits, they may lash out at you because they feel this criticism. This is true even if you don't say a word: many of us pick up on other people's judgments.

They can feel your criticism, just as you can feel their criticism, too. So be positive, be proactive, and enlist your family and friends' support. But ask because they love you and want you to be healthy, not because you're a savior holding the answers to all their health problems.

4

Chapter Four

THE DETOX

Congratulations. The weeks of preparation have paid off. You're feeling strong, committed and ready to move forward with your sugar abstinence: you're ready to give up sugar for good.

The next few weeks will be the most physically challenging as your body adjusts to the chemical changes of giving up sugar. I call it "sugar detox," because it is, in many ways, a detox. But don't let the challenges of the next few weeks dissuade you. While you may feel awful for a few days, the discomfort will pass. Once you're not eating sugar, you'll be amazed at how differently you feel, including how you feel towards sugar. In this chapter, I'm going to take you through your sugar detox, step by step. There's light at the end of the tunnel: at the end of this phase, you'll be sugar free.

Having said that, I've also talked to many people who've given up sugar and it wasn't nearly as hard as they thought it would be. They found it surprisingly easy. So this is another example of how each experience is different. You may find that giving up sugar isn't that big of a deal for you, either. Good for you.

Step One: Eliminate The Hidden Sugars

You may be aware of the sugar in your favorite candy bar. But what about the sugar in your salad dressing, your spaghetti sauce, or in your energy bar? When you begin your sugar detox, it's important that you truly eliminate all forms of sugar from your diet. If you're buying any packaged, processed foods, look for the following forms of sugar:

Agave	Barley malt
Beet sugar	Brown sugar
Cane sugar	Carob syrup
Corn syrup solids	Corn syrup
Date sugar	Diatase
Diastatic malt	Dextrose
Ethyl Maltol	Fructose
Fruit juice	Fruit sweetener
Galactose	Glucose
Glucose solids	Grape sugar
High fructose corn syrup	Honey
Invert sugar	Lactose
Malt syrup	Malto-dextrin
Maltose	Mannitol
Maple sugar or maple syrup	Molasses
Raw sugar	Refiner's syrup

Rice Sugar   Sorbitol
Sucrose   Turbinado sugar

To give up sugar for good, it's important to give up all forms of sugar...even these sneaky ones.

It's also important to look at how your body reacts to foods that may not look like sugar - like white flour foods such as white bread, or refined carbohydrates like potato chips - but that act like sugar in your body. Some sugar sensitive people actually prefer starchy carbohydrates to sugary carbohydrates, eating lots of pizza, pasta, bread, pastries, and chips. If you're giving up other forms of sugar, but eating lots of white bread and potato chips, your body may not notice the difference. In other words, you may have simply traded one form of sugar for another.

This was true in my life. While I had been sugar free for a long time, I was still eating lots and lots of tortilla chips: my sugar substitute. When I stopped eating tortilla chips, I was shocked at my body's reaction: I went through a tortilla chip detox! I experienced all of the mood swings, up and down emotions, sugar cravings, irritability, and sadness that I experienced when I gave up sugar. But after the first few days without tortilla chips, I started to feel like myself again, my moods stabilized, and I no longer craved my treat.

How deep you want to take your sugar detox is up to you. Maybe, for now, you just want to focus on sugar. Then, once you've maintained your sugar abstinence for several months, you'll tackle the other simple carbs. Or, you can eliminate all forms of sugar at the same time, including refined carbohydrates. The choice is yours. There isn't a wrong answer. But from my experience, I can say that I didn't achieve all of the benefits of sugar free living until I gave up all forms of sugar - including white flour.

Step Two: Pick A Good Time

Now that you're ready to give up sugar, I want to offer a suggestion on timing. The first week without sugar can be challenging. In effect, you'll be detoxing. Be kind to yourself: this is not the week to tackle an important work project, to confront a family member about a major argument, or to potty train your toddler. Pick a calm, low-key week, where you can get extra rest, take naps, call on some help with co-workers, and even have a day to yourself, if you need to. Find ways to limit your stress. See if you can clear your schedule. Maybe you take a few vacation days and stay home. Maybe you can arrange for some extra help with childcare - can a friend help you out with a few play dates?

Don't pick the week of Christmas, Thanksgiving, Easter, Halloween, or Valentine's Day. You don't want any extra temptations to make your sugar detox more difficult than it needs to be. If you severely crave sugar in the winter, maybe it's best to wait until springtime, when the days are longer, you're more active and the weather is warmer. I would also recommend that women watch their monthly cycles, as many women crave sweets the week before their period. The week right after my period was the easiest time for me to give up sugar.

Step Three: Prepare Your Family

If you've already talked to your family and loved ones, they should already be pretty well prepared. You may want to further prepare them now that you are embarking on your abstinence. Arrange a family meeting or another time when you can explain to them what they can expect during your first week without sugar.

Here's What You Need To Tell Them

As you may have observed, I'm sensitive to sugar. I feel like I can't stop once I start eating it. It's almost like a food allergy and something I need to stop eating.

I've decided to stop eating sugar. In the coming week, I'll be going through withdrawal as I experience the first few days without eating any sugar. This will be a challenging time for me, and I'd love to have your support.

For the first few days, I may be tired, irritable, or weepy. I may experience strong cravings for sugar. I may be grumpy or angry. This will pass. In the meantime, I'll need to be extra vigilant about keeping sugar out of sight.

Give them specific action "to dos" they can do to help you like, "Can we eat dinner at 6 p.m. every night? Waiting too long to eat is really hard for me." Or, "can you keep your ice cream in the basement freezer so I don't see it?"

If you'll be behaving differently, you may say something like, "I won't be doing any baking this week. I'm sorry if you feel disappointed."

If you know that you have a particularly tricky time when you'll need extra support, ask for it. Say, "Will you take a walk with me after work so I'm not tempted to have sugar at that time?"

Then reassure them that the initial challenges will fade. Reassure them that this is not about trying to control what they eat. You may say, "I'm not asking any of you to give up sugar or to change your eating habits. Once I've been sugar abstinent for several weeks, we should be able to have sugar in the house without it affecting me."

It's up to you how much you share with those outside of your home, people like friends, co-workers, and extended family. I didn't share with these people because I was a stay at home mom when I gave up sugar and I spent most of my time at home. You may have different needs if you're working outside the home.

Step Four: Line Up A Support Team

A friend can help you buy time between the impulse to eat sugar and your desire to act on it.

Have a friend that is willing to call you and support you during your first few days without sugar. You may not need this step: you may be okay on your own. But if the brownies are calling your name, and you're one step away from shoving one in your mouth, it would be beneficial to have a friend you can call to talk you out of a slip.

You may also want to create a list of sugar substitutes, things you can do when you're craving sugar. This can include things like leaving the kitchen and going outside, taking a walk, going for a bike ride, or reading a book.

Step Five: Create A Supportive Environment

Remember that list of foods with hidden sugars in step one? Now is the time to go through your home and eliminate these foods. When I went through my sugar detox, I cleared my home of the biggies: chocolate, ice cream, candy, and raisins. However, I did leave a few things in the house with sugar in them, such as ketchup, as these weren't tempting to me. But ketchup may tempt you, and may have to go, for now. You know what you eat, what you crave, and your willpower. Don't be afraid to really dejunk the house (you can remind your family that this is a temporary measure.) Don't be afraid to skip the usual ice cream store visit or coffeehouse visit if you're unsure of being able to avoid temptation.

I kept some of my family's sugar treats in the house for their use, but I did ask them to hide them from me! This was a win-win for our family.

Step Six: Keep Up Your Foundation Behaviors

Keep eating three regular meals a day, including breakfast, and have protein with your meals. Get plenty of sleep. You may feel more fatigued than usual during your first week without sugar, as your body adjusts to your new way of eating. I certainly did.

Continue to exercise if you can, although don't feel guilty if your normal pep is missing. I had a lot of lethargy those first few days and exercised very lightly. Walking is always good.

Make sure you're taking a quality vitamin/mineral supplement. L-Glutamine is an amino acid that helps minimize sugar cravings. (You can buy it at health food stores and on amazon.com). I took this once a day (in the afternoons, when I typically experienced my greatest sugar cravings) during my first week without sugar and found it helpful. Julia Ross, the author of *The Mood Cure*, offers information in her book about supplementing with amino acids.

Step Seven: Begin!

You're probably feeling very motivated right now, ready to kick this pesky sugar habit. Channel that motivation and use it to your advantage this first week.

Sugar affects brain neurotransmitters the same way that alcohol does. Eating sugar causes a temporary release of feel good chemicals in the brain, such as dopamine, serotonin and beta-endorphins. (Read Kathleen Des Maisons' book *Potatoes not Prozac* for more information on how sugar creates an addictive response in the body.) When you eliminate sugar, your body experiences a withdrawal from those feel good chemicals. Eventually, your body adjusts. But the reason you may feel so awful these first few days is that your brain is literally undergoing a chemical shift.

There are some experts who suspect that sugar addicts are naturally low in those neurotransmitters, especially serotonin. In effect, sugar addicts are using sugar to boost their mood, even though the short term gain leads to the long term, painful despair of sugar addiction.

Here's How A Typical Sugar Detox Unfolds

Day 1: Your motivation is high. You're feeling good. You're excited to see what sugar free living feels like. You find it easy to ignore your sugar cravings. Physically, you may be experiencing fatigue, headaches, and some drowsiness, but it's tolerable.

Day 2: Your motivation is still high, but you may be feeling worse than day one. You may be feeling run down or have a sense of malaise. You may feel bitchy or irritable or easily angered. You may feel sad or depressed.

If you're desperate for a sweet hit, have one small piece of low GI Fruit, like an apple or a serving of berries. If you think that fruit will only spark your sugar cravings, abstain. But do not eat dried fruit or any sugar: it will put you right back at square one. I actually found it easier to not eat fruit while detoxing, but that's my experience. Even the natural sugars in fruit triggered my desire for more sugar.

Day 3 and 4: These are the toughest days, in my opinion. The sugar cravings are the worst on days 3 and 4, but if you can hang in there until day 5, they usually disappear. Mentally, you may feel like you're on a roller coaster ride, coasting up and down through a wide gamut of emotions, from irritability, to anger, to sadness, to despair. Your skin may be breaking out. You may feel like you have a terrible case of PMS. You may feel inside out, like you're even losing your mind. Hang in there. This will all pass.

Day 5-7: Your physical cravings for sugar should be fading dramatically. You may be suprised how much you aren't craving your normal treats. Your moods are stabilizing; you're starting to feel like "yourself" again. Your fatigue should be easing as your body adjusts to a sugar free diet. You're cautious and curious if you can stick with your sugar free diet over the long term.

I've made a list of withdrawal symptoms that you may experience those first five to seven days as you detox off sugar. Remember, you may not experience all, or any, of these things. I share them with you so that you can feel prepared if you do experience them, to reassure you that you aren't crazy, you aren't losing your mind, these are just the side effects of giving up sugar.

If you are concerned about any of your symptoms, please seek out medical support.

Here are some common side effects of sugar detox:

Headaches (particularly if you're giving up caffeine, too)
Drowsiness
Skin breakouts
A snotty nose or feeling of a cold
Depression

Mood swings
Irritability
Anger
Impatience - a feeling of lashing out at the slightest provocation
Anxiety
Fatigue or lack of energy
Despair
An increased appetite
A feeling of being easily upset or brought to tears
Indigestion or other stomach discomforts

If you experience suicidal thoughts, severe anxiety or depression, or any other serious medical problems, please contact a doctor immediately.

After your first week or two without sugar, you should notice an absence of physical cravings. Your appetite and moods should stabilize. Your digestion should normalize. If your skin broke out, it should be clearing up. (Sugar is very inflammatory.) You should experience a new level of health and vitality.

If you aren't feeling significantly better, two things can be going on

1. It may take your body longer to process the toxins from years of sugar abuse. Stick with your sugar abstinence for another week, and then see how you feel.

2. You may be substituting covert sugars for overt ones. If you've given up ice cream and candy, but you're still overeating potato chips, tortilla chips, or white bread, you've merely traded one type of sugar - ice cream and chocolate - for another - white flour. In order to reap the benefits of sugar free living, you need to eliminate all sugars from your diet, including your beloved white bread. Eliminate the sneaky white flour, and processed, refined carbs, in addition to the sugar, and then see how you feel.

Here are some points to consider, things that eased the discomfort of the sugar detox for me

1. **Remember the discomfort is temporary**. If you're feeling really badly on day 3 or 4, it's easy to project these feelings forward: If this is what sugar free living is like, forget it! But that's like saying that parenthood feels the same as childbirth. How you feel after your sugar detox is much different than how you feel during your sugar detox. Take your sugar detox one day at a time, one hour at a time, one craving at a time.

2. **Remember why you're doing this**. When I gave up sugar, I made a conscious decision to trade my desire for sweets for mental health. Sugar was literally making me crazy. When I chose sugar abstinence as a way of life, I chose peace and mental clarity over sugar, obsessive thoughts, and depression. Those first few days, when I felt tempted to eat sugar, I reminded myself that my decision to give up sugar was about regaining my very life. I would talk to myself and say, "Which are you choosing: your mental health, or sugar?" That was usually enough to keep me on track.

3. **Talk yourself down from your cravings**. Just because your mind says you "have" to have a sugar hit, doesn't mean you have to listen to it. In my experience, cravings are like waves. They start small, and then they build to a crescendo - at which point you do feel like you'll die without a bite of something sweet - only to crest and ebb back to nothing.

Ride the waves. Let yourself experience the intensity of a craving while talking yourself through it: *Yes, I know you feel like you'll die without eating that cake, but you can feel this craving without giving in.*

Giving up sugar for good means a willingness to feel your feelings - even those difficult emotions like craving, or anger, or anxiety, without stuffing them with sugar. Take the first step by acknowledging your cravings - Yes, I hear your need for sugar - without giving in. Cravings typically last about 20 minutes, at which point they dwindle back to nothingness. Find something else to do for those 20 minutes - phone a friend, exercise, go for a walk, play with your kids. Each time you face a sugar craving and choose to abstain, you prove to yourself that you are stronger than your sugar cravings, which fuels your confidence for the next time.

For more information on taming cravings, I offer sugar programs at suga-raddictionbook.com where I teach you my process of "rocking your cravings to sleep" and softening cravings by leaning into them.

4. **You may feel worse before your feel better**. As poet Robert Frost wrote, "The only way out is through." The only way to experience the freedom that comes with sugar abstinence is to go through the process of giving it up. And unfortunately, that process usually entails feeling worse before you feel better. Again, perspective is the key: what is one week of discomfort when compared to the many, many weeks - *no, years* - of excellent health you'll experience from sugar free living? I know it's hard. I know it hurts. Offer yourself care when you're hurting. Put your hand on your heart and tell yourself, "I care about your pain. I care about your suffering." Sit with your pain while you also recognize it will pass.

We have a remarkable ability to face pain when we feel supported, heard and acknowledged. Caring for your pain creates these feelings of support.

5. **Add extra structure**. If you find that you're overly tempted to eat sugar or to skip meals, put yourself on a schedule. Eat every three to four hours, setting a timer as a reminder, if necessary. Plan your meals if you don't like coming home to the panic of, "What's for dinner?"

This is not the week to buy a pizza at the last minute because you haven't planned anything and are overhungry. I found it helpful to plan out every day's meals ahead of time. I'd make a menu of what I would eat for breakfast, lunch and dinner and make sure that my fridge was stocked with the proper ingredients.

Meals that worked for me included roast chicken with a large salad, salmon with sautéed vegetables, pinto beans, sautéed peppers, onions and greens, and a grilled steak with sautéed mushrooms, a baked potato and steamed broccoli. If you do go out to eat during this first week, ask lots of questions and choose a restaurant that will have something that you can eat.

6. **Have non sugar treats on hand**. Macadamia nut butter is one of my favorite no-sugar treats. So are tamari almonds, greek style yogurt and plain kefir with almonds. I always kept these treats on hand during my sugar detox so I could have a dessert or after dinner treat if I was feeling desperate.

Non sugar treats should also include treats that aren't food related. Often we turn to comfort food when what we really want is comfort. If this has been a longstanding pattern in your life, your journey will include inquiry into why you've undernourished yourself. While it's a process that takes time, every instance that you offer yourself true comfort instead of food, you give yourself proof that you are capable of nurturing yourself in non-food ways. This builds up, over time, becoming an ingrained habit. You gain confidence in your ability to handle life's pain without sugar, without food.

7. **Find a stress release activity that you can commit to everyday**. While you may be feeling gung ho the first few days of your sugar detox, and while you may be able to shelter yourself from your normal routine during this time, you can't put off the nitty gritty of life forever.

While you can find ways to minimize the stress in your life, at some point, life gets messy. The dog will puke all over the carpet, the water heater will break, or you'll get stuck in traffic. Stuff happens.

It's important for you to have ways of coping with stress so that you don't turn to sugar in a moment of crisis. Exercise is a great stress reliever. So is proper sleep: everything gets blown out of proportion when you're tired. Yoga, meditation and deep belly breathing are also helpful ways to lower stress.

Giving up sugar is an ongoing, lifelong process. It's not something we can check off our lists and complete once. Its long term success depends on the daily habits of our lives - habits like nourishing ourselves regularly with food, rest, care and soothing. We don't do these things perfectly. No one does. But we stay committed to regularly checking in with ourselves and caring for our tender, precious human bodies.

8. **Give up your weight loss goals, for now.** I know that you probably want to lose weight, in addition to giving up sugar. But it's important to focus on one goal at a time. Right now, your primary focus should be on giving up sugar. That may mean putting aside your weight loss goals for now.

Giving up sugar may throw your metabolism a bit out of whack. You may find yourself very hungry those first one to two weeks without sugar as your body adjusts to your new way of eating. You may find yourself over-eating non-sugar foods as you stop eating sugar. This is all very normal.

It's important to eat regularly during this time so that your blood sugar stays stabilized and your sugar cravings recede. It will be very, very hard to resist sugar if you're also dieting at the same time and consciously limiting your food. My recommendation is to get off the sugar first. Then, when you're no longer hooked on the sugar, you can gently work at losing the extra weight.

I know this is hard. We want to be healed, pronto. We want the evidence of our overeating pain to just go away. Now. Our egos take a beating when we put aside the weight loss goals. But it's the best way I found to heal. I would even say it's necessary. If our self care is only motivated by vanity - which is motivated by fear, a false belief in our unworthiness and unlovableness - we will stay trapped in food.

After I gave up sugar I realized how my overeating was fueled by sugar high expectations for my body. I wanted to be the "best" version of myself - which meant my lowest possible healthy weight. These standards were nearly impossible to meet and took much of my energy and time to try and meet them. It was as if every meal was a final exam I had to pass with an A plus.

So when I failed - which was anything less than 100%, and therefore often - it triggered a "what the hell" effect and a binge. Then it was the end of the world because my body wouldn't be as "thin" now that I'd eaten 3 plates worth of food. So I'd get hooked back into eating super, super clean because I *had* to have that body and I had to make up for my "slip." Around and around I went.

How do we break the pattern?

Start with the sugar. That's what I did. I got off the sugar and then I dove into my overeating and my perfectionism with my body. Ironically, freeing myself from this need to be the "best" version of myself, to have this super lean, super fit, super beautiful body, reinforced my decision to stay off sugar. My sugar abstinence was motivated by love, not ego, not vanity, and my expectations relaxed. With this softening, when I did eat sugar - inadvertantly or not - it wasn't the end of the world. It wouldn't trigger the "what the hell" sugar binge. I found much more steadiness; the "progress not perfection" they teach in 12 step programs.

9. **Accept your limits**. When I was detoxing off sugar, I found ways to be kind to myself, to make my sugar detox as easy as possible. This meant that I avoided the candy aisles at the grocery store, I paid at the pump for my gas so I wouldn't have to walk by the candy in the gas station, and I abstained from baking or making any desserts.

These are examples of being honest and knowing your limits. These are examples of what I shared earlier in the book about minimizing triggers and overarousal.

Think of ways that you can make your detox easy. Maybe you skip your weekly get together at the coffee house, choosing to meet your girlfriends for a walk instead. Maybe you stay clear of the break room at work with the vending machines and donuts. Maybe you ask your spouse to go to the grocery store with you so you aren't tempted to sneak a treat while you're there. Perhaps you golf with your buddies instead of going out for drinks.

Whatever your decision, don't think that being honest about your limits is proof of weakness. Sometimes we think that being sugar free means never admitting we have a craving or are wanting sugar for soothing. We think we need to somehow erase our desire for sugar and minimize it. Then we end up fighting with ourselves, trying to control life, and labeling ourselves as "bad" because of our feelings.

Don't fight your desires. Embrace them. Care for them.

Care for them by recognizing, "I'm getting hooked here" and reaching out for support so that you can ride the wave. Be willing to say, "I'm human and I'm feeling challenged right now. Will you help me?"

This is an act of tremendous courage. It takes bravery to be honest about our sticking points. It takes humility to ask for help, reach out, and be vulnerable. It takes honesty - how am I feeling versus how I think I *should* be feeling?

These virtues create sugar sobriety and ease our fears about being perfect. You gain confidence and realize, "I can do this." You stop needing to control and you invite those moments of craving as teachers. You are aware of your limits and you heed them. This is a sure sign of maturity, of growing up.

10. **Track your progress**. If you're someone who likes a lot of immediate, positive feedback, a sugar detox can be challenging because you feel terrible before you feel better. One way to counter this is by writing down your successes in a blank notebook. Abby Seixas, author of *Finding the Deep River Within*, calls these tools "victory logs."

For example, if you had a strong craving for sugar and you choose to take a walk instead, write it down. If you had an argument with your spouse and you stopped yourself from eating sugar - your typical pattern - write it down. If you're having a day when you're feeling discouraged, and doubting your ability to stick with your sugar abstinence, reread your journal to give yourself the encouragement you need.

11. **Give yourself manageable goals**. In the beginning, you have to take your sugar abstinence one day at a time. It's overwhelming to look at this as forever. It feels too daunting.

Focus on just today. That's all you have.

Then the next day, focus on getting through that day.

Then tackle the next.

If you look too far ahead, it's easy to panic: *I can't do this!* You'll feel over-whelmed. You're anticipating future pain. Whenever we anticipate future pain, we make it harder than it needs to be. We imagine all kind of painful scenarios - scenarios that haven't happened!

When we look to the future and believe, "It's too hard!" we're looking at sugar abstinence through sugar addicted eyes. After you've gone through your sugar detox, and you aren't experiencing the daily sugar cravings, sugar free living will feel more manageable.

Focus on this present moment. Get out of your head and into your body. Do a body scan. How are you feeling? Where is there tightness? Discom-fort? Ease? Lightness? Getting into the body is a way to get out of thought and our anxiety about future pain.

Remind yourself why you're doing this. What benefits do you hope to gain? Make a list, everything from feeling comfortable in a bathing suit to having stable moods to being a better parent. Keep this list handy. On days when your motivation is flagging, read it and remind yourself that giving up sugar goes beyond sugar itself.

12. **Count each victory**. It's easy to become end-focused, to define success as complete sugar abstinence, discounting all the many victories you have in between. But every day can be a success.

We are always in process. Enjoy the process. Live the process. Don't wait for someday. Enjoy each new sensation and each moment of healing.

Every time you crave sugar but don't give in, that's a success. Every time you choose an apple over ice cream, that is a success. Every time that you get up and make breakfast, that is a success. It's a success even if things fall apart at 3 p.m.

Count and honor them all.

We're so hard on ourselves. We overlook all the times we sit in the hot seat and sit with our sugar cravings without giving in, while we notice every slip and make it the end of the world.

Change is hard. It hurts. It's uncomfortable.

Honor every small change and moment of courage.

Celebrate every positive change so that one slip up doesn't obliterate your other successes. Pay attention to them. Pause and experience them. We often speed through and rush on ahead to get somewhere, so our daily victories feel meaningless. They feel meaningless when we aren't paying attention. They don't count because we discount them.

Slow down. Pay attention. Pay attention to the feel of your breakfast on your tongue, the texture of your food, the feeling of going to bed without bingeing. Pay attention to the feeling of lightness - the lightness of spirit - that you feel surging in your daily habits.

When you do slip up, let yourself be human. Don't let one slip cancel out dozens of successes. Feel your sadness, hold your regret, and remind yourself, "It's a journey." You're not rushing anywhere. Every step - and every misstep - has value. They have value because they are your life. Are you living it?

13. **If you slip up and eat sugar, practice compassion**. What about when you do slip up? What if you give into the brownie after four or five days without sugar?

Forgive yourself. You're human. You made a mistake. Let it go. Shame, beating yourself up, drama, and despair: all of those things are counterproductive and keep you from having the courage to stay away from eating sugar.

Interestingly enough, we beat ourselves up to make ourselves feel better, to soothe our sadness about slipping. We think that punishing ourselves will somehow get us back on track and reinforce our desire to change. We think it's motivation!

When we whip ourselves with criticism and blame, we reinforce our drive for sugar. It's an excuse to binge! We feel so bad, what else can we do? That's what we tell ourseles. So beating ourselves up can be a way to stay stuck, a sneaky attempt to sabotage ourselves from having to change. We beat ourselves up so we don't have to change. I say this very gently, because we often aren't aware of this. I often turned a slip into an excuse to binge on sugar for days or weeks. I figured as long as I'm being bad, I might as well as be *really* bad. As long as I'd fallen off the wagon, I may as well enjoy myself. And then I would feel terrible....for bingeing, again.

The way out of this cycle is compassion. We can forgive ourselves, hold our feelings with tenderness, and recognize that life goes on. We'll always have another opportunity.

We need to face our true pain. Beating ourselves up is a poor substitute. Better to cry our tears, feel our sadness, mourn our regret and face the real pain than to cover it up with "whippings." Hold your hand on your heart and ask yourself, "What am I feeling?" Care for those feelings. Keep your hand on your heart and tell youself, "I care. I care for this pain."

I love this ritual. It not only soothes my pain but creates feelings of deep intimacy with myself.

After you've tended to your heart, tend to your body. From a physical standpoint, I always found it helpful to eat light meals with some protein after a sugar binge. I also liked to drink some peppermint tea, soothing to the stomach. Brushing your teeth is a great way to signal to your body that you're done eating. You can also leave the kitchen or the house if you have to. Phone a friend. Write in your journal.

With your heart and body cared for, then tend to your head. It is only after my feelings are cared for and heard that I can examine the situation with enough distance to uncover truth. (I find this true for all intellectual exercises - I find them most productive *after* I've felt, held and processed my feelings.)

Examine the feelings and patterns that led to the sugar. What did you learn? What was going on? What would you do differently next time?

14. **Trust yourself.** Trust your goodness. Trust your desire to heal.

Believe that you can do this. Believe that you are strong. Believe that if you're at a party and a hostess is offering a piece of her famous homemade cheesecake, that you can smile politely and say, "No thank you."

Trust that you'll be able to find non sugar ways to fill your life with sweetness. Trust that you'll appreciate the benefits of sugar free living, and that you won't go back to the up and down emotions, the weight gain, and the poor health of sugar addiction.

Often, we're afraid of making commitments - especially a big commitment, like giving up sugar - because we're afraid we'll fail. We avoid what we most fear - which is pain.

Giving up sugar may frighten you. You may think it's going to hurt. That's okay. It's normal.

Care for your fear. Comfort it. Have compassion for it. It's part of the human condition - we all feel afraid at times.

Let someone hold you when you feel especially fearful. Let someone sit with you and help you process your fear so you don't have to do it alone. Offer all your feelings your tenderness, love and compassion.

The ironic thing about fear is that it softens with action. Moving towards our fear - and not moving away from it as we might think - is what makes it ebb, flow and dissipate. It's how we find the courage to act, change and grow.

5

Chapter Five

WHAT TO EAT

The most pressing question people have when they cut out sugar is: What do I eat? Does cutting out sugar mean I have to give up all carbs? Flour? What can I have for breakfast? Can I eat bread? What do I feed my kids? What can I eat at restaurants, parties and at social events?

I think the deeper, underlying question is: How can I have a relaxed, pleasurable, joyful relationship with food even while there are some foods I'm choosing not to eat? And this: How do I know whether a food triggers my sugar sensitivity because of its unique properties or whether it's my own habit of turning to food for comfort that triggers overeating?

It is possible to have both abstinence *and* a relaxed approach to food. It may take time to get there – it did for me. And it's still a worthy, realistic and approachable goal.

While what triggers a sugar reaction is different for each person, and is based on your unique biology, I'll offer a glimpse into my own life. This is what works for me. I offer these suggestions as a guideline, not hard and fast rules.

I'll also share how I learned to separate overeating that stemmed from eating sugar from overeating that was behaviorally based.

Fearing food and food rules

In your quest for greater health, you've probably read many nutrition books. If you read enough of them, they contradict one another. This is because there is no consensus on food.

I see this not as something problematic, but as a reflection of the fact that we're all different, with different needs, motivations, and approaches to food. We're individuals, not animals in a research lab.

And yet it creates a lot of confusion. There's a tremendous amount of food dogma out there - a lot of noise in the area of nutrition and diet.

One expert says to eat vegan, another high protein. Someone says don't eat fruit; someone else says eat as much fruit as you want. One advises raw food, another low carb. When you're overeating, you also get caught between those who say eat everything you want in moderation and those who say abstain from your trigger foods.

It's enough to make you feel crazy, jostled from the ping pong of opposing ideas. It can make you feel weak, helpless and lost – like you have no clue how to care for your body.

It can lead to a chronic sense of anxiety that "you aren't doing it right." You can fear every food as a potential "enemy," as something that can trigger sugar sensitivity or a binge.

This feeds a constant striving for new information. You may read every new nutrition book that's published, looking for "the" diet that will solve all your food issues for good. You never feel safe. You always wonder if "something's missing" in your food plan, and so you continue to read and study to find the missing piece.

I know because I did this for many, many years. I was addicted to the latest nutrition book that hit bookstore shelves; to every weight loss article in a magazine. I had to read it – there might be something I was "missing." I didn't trust my own inner wisdom, my ability to listen to my body and respond appropriately. I didn't trust my ability to apply what I was learning to my body to see if it made sense for me. So I constantly sought "more" – more knowledge, more theories, more ideas from out there.

I had no center.

Soothing our fears about healing from food

It was only after I stopped seeking and sat with my restless searching that I could see my behavior for what it was – a quest for a definitive answer about what to eat that would finally solve all my overeating problems and give me the body I wanted. I wanted to be "cured." I wanted to look a certain way, and I wanted to find a way to eat that would guarantee I could always have that body.

I wanted to be a certain way, too - completely healed from food stuff - and I wanted to find a way to eat that would guarantee my "success."

I wanted a formula that would guarantee that I would never, ever, ever suffer again from food stuff - that I would never again have to think about what I put in my mouth.

I was looking for an escape from reality. I wanted the golden ticket that would somehow make me exempt from the normal trials and travails that accompany every human life.

This is different than a heartfelt desire for healing. What I'm talking about is a desire to control, to appear in charge, to be "together."

It's taken me many years of practice and unhooking to soften this habit. Over time, I've been able to gently let go of the nutrition seeking. I started by putting on my pause button when I saw the weight loss headlines on magazines at the grocery store check out aisle. I had to actively resist the pull of, "But maybe there's something really, really helpful there that I haven't read anywhere else!"

I did this by sitting with my anxiety and my desire for more "knowledge" to inquire, "What's really here?" I stopped trying to soothe my feelings by reading the diet article and sat with them. I felt my fear that I would never have freedom from food "stuff." I felt my fear that I'm broken and fundamentally flawed and have some biological reason why I can't sit down and eat without stuffing myself to oblivion. I felt my fear that I would never learn how to listen to my body. I felt my fear that I would always be addicted to sugar.

I sat with my feelings and offered them my care and comfort. I would breathe and sometimes put my hand on my heart, depending on how busy the grocery store was and how unobtrusively I could do this.

I would sit with my feelings and feel my fear instead of trying to immediately make it go away. In doing this, I would feel my fear soften. I would often find grief underneath fear – grief that I struggle so much with something as basic as food; grief that it's so hard for me; grief that I have to focus so much on my own basic care. Grief that I'm human and don't have all my stuff together.

I would sit – stay with them - and offer these feelings care, too.

As I continued to care for my feelings and feel them instead of pushing them away, I found the itch to read the magazine article soften. I could soften the habit and buy my groceries without throwing in the magazine or sneaking a peek while waiting to check out.

Soothing the need for food knowledge

By practicing this many, many, many times, I've found that I no longer feel so pulled to read the magazine article or the nutrition book. The itch is often there – the desire to seek out "the answer" and the curiosity of, "What's underneath that cover?"

But the pull to scratch the itch and act on it by buying the book or magazine has subsided. I've subtly shifted the pattern – not by trying to control it, not with will power, not by making myself feel bad, and not by creating a rule about how I can't read nutrition books. I shifted the pattern by feeling the feelings underneath the desire and caring for the feelings. *By caring for my feelings internally, I softened my need to care for my feelings externally.*

Sometimes I do succumb. More often that not, it's from a place of intention rather than a place of compulsion. There's a subtle difference. One is fear based; one is based on self-trust, following my inner wisdom.

Soothing our food cravings

It's the exact same process to soften your cravings and desire for sugar. You can stop, pause and ask yourself, "What am I feeling? What's here? What is the real need I'm trying to meet?" when you find yourself feeling an insatiable desire to eat a gallon of ice cream. (This process is most helpful after you've detoxed from sugar, as you aren't feeling the biochemical craving for sugar.)

You may discover that you want to eat sugar because you're feeling anxious about paying for your child's school fees. This anxiety has deeper layers of feeling in it. You may have grief – sadness about your diminished finances; you may feel anger about your financial circumstances; you may feel fearful that your finances won't change. On the deepest level, you may feel afraid that your money problems are a sign that you're irresponsible, that you've somehow failed Adulthood 101. It's a basic fear many of us have some version of, this sense of, "This (fill in the blank) means I'm not okay."

You can see how eating ice cream is a heck of a lot easier than uncovering what's there. And yet eating the ice cream is like reading the magazine article - an external attempt to care for your feelings. It's actually a way of avoiding your feelings, because you can focus on the ice cream, on its taste and delight, instead of the tightening in your belly about the upcoming bill. And then if the ice cream leads to a binge, then you can focus on that problem and that pain, and completely avoid feeling the grief you feel about your inability to pay the tuition.

Creating internal sanctuary

We are so afraid of pain. And yet our avoidance of pain causes more pain than facing the pain itself. If you sit with your feelings and peel the onion, peeling layer after layer of feeling, and offering each feeling care and compassion, you'll feel the hurt. You'll feel the hurt and you'll also feel your caring for your hurt, which is what finally gives you the soothing you're truly seeking. You'll feel the need to soothe the hurt externally - with the ice cream - softening. You'll see your habitual pattern of turning to sugar or food soften in the face of this beautiful caring, in this gentle holding of your vulnerability.

Finally facing the fear of, "Am I lovable and okay in my imperfection?" is how we find true refuge. It's how we find an internal sense of sanctuary instead of seeking outward sanctuary in chocolate, cookies, cakes and pies. It's how we stop fighting against cravings for sugar and looking at them as the enemy.

It's how we befriend our craving and wanting, to see it as something tender in ourselves. We can see a craving not as something to arm ourselves against but as an invitation to stop, pause and ask, "What am I feeling? What's here?" It's an invitation to create healing, to find wholeness, to turn our attention inwards and rest in our sanctuary.

How we approach sugar

Our fears about food can affect how we approach sugar. We may decide to stop eating sugar not because we notice its negative effect on our bodies but because we're trying to soothe our anxiety over this uncomfortable feeling of "I'm missing out on something." We want to feel like we have the answers – a very normal, natural human response to the ambiguity of life.

We want to make life feel more certain and predictable. We like having a measure of our health under our control. We want to feel like we have some of the inherent ambiguity of life a little bit more tamed and figured out.

It's why many of us feel better when our closets are organized, our bills paid, our ducks in a row.

We're looking for safety – but a false safety – a safety based on things outside of ourselves: control of our external environment, strict food rules, and the elimination of as many possible dietary pitfalls (read: temptations) as possible.

We think that if we stop eating sugar we will finally have the answer. We will never, ever have another food craving, eat emotionally, gain weight, or overeat. We will age beautifully and gracefully and look 10 years younger than our counterparts.

Again - this is not about health. This is not about honestly trying to heal our sugar addiction. This is about fear and minimizing fear.

Controlling to stay sugar free

Because staying off sugar is so important and so necessary, we will then do anything we can to safeguard it. We think that if we structure our environment just so, and are really, really, really disciplined, and watch ourselves – and life – like a hawk, we will never, ever eat another bite of junk food or sugar again.

This is how this can look:

Whenever we overeat a certain food, like, say bananas, we put it on the banned foods list, the good and bad food lists we carry around in our heads.

Bananas must be bad – because why else would we overeat them? They must have too many natural sugars in them, we think. So we give them up.

A few days later, we binge on a baked potato. Potatoes are bad. Natural sugars. Too much starch. We put them on the bad food list.

We keep approaching food in this way until all we are left with on our "good" food list is celery and chicken breasts.

So we think – ah! That must mean that all I can eat is non-starchy vegetables and meat. We hold a hammer – abstinence - and every food craving is a nail – a food we have to abstain from. Abstinence becomes a tool that we use in every context.

We try and eat this way for as long as we can. We focus on controlling the food and controlling the cravings and trying to minimize our exposure to all those bad, bad, bad foods. Our life feels small and tight and primarily focused on what we put in our mouths – which it is.

We feel exhausted by trying to manage so much. We are worn out. We are bored senseless with our food. We are tired of always telling ourselves, "No, you can't eat that. No, not that either." We're feeling the first inklings of deprivation and resentment that there is so much pleasure in food – and in life – that is not ours.

Over time, we start to wonder: Is this what being sugar free feels like? Is it even worth it? We get fed up. We decide, better to be obsessed with food and eat sugar and have some pleasure than to be obsessed with food and have no pleasure and abstain from sugar.

In both examples, we're focused on food – on what we can eat or what we can't eat. In both cases, we don't feel free because food takes up so much of our mental bandwidth.

When to use external controls

This is where it may get tricky, and where I'm going to try to be very clear. In some circumstances, external controls are the most compassionate and wisest response. External controls can be helpful and are even necessary in the beginning stages of going off sugar. You may need really strong boundaries around what you can and can't eat, a regular, consistent eating schedule, and structured meals when you're first unhooking from sugar.

I'm not saying give up all external controls, structures, or boundaries. Boundaries and controls absolutely have their place. But when we use them in an attempt to safeguard ourselves against life – which is incredibly dynamic, impermanent, and inherently incontrollable – we suffer. When we use them as a substitute for necessary, deeper healing work – such as looking at our tendency to turn to food for solace – we're using them to hide, not grow. It's a cop out from doing the hard work of facing our stuff.

The same external controls that assist us in the beginning stages of our journey cripple us if we don't release them as we grow out of them. To find true freedom from food, we have to find ways to stop turning to food in the first place. We can't do this if we're always looking at food as the problem.

Taking off the training wheels

I liken it to training wheels. Training wheels are helpful to overcome the fear of learning how to ride a bike. They lower the learning curve to make it approachable. We use training wheels like keeping sugar out of the house, minimizing our exposure to certain foods, and protecting ourselves against pitfalls in order to go through the initial separation from sugar.

And yet like a child who never takes the training wheels off, we will keep ourselves from experiencing tremendous joy and freedom if we don't recognize when it's time to let our crutches go.

You can't go flying down a hill at the same speed with training wheels on. You may feel protected from danger but you also protect yourself from a much greater range of experiences – starting with the experience of growing out of our safety zones.

Experimenting with food

What does taking our training wheels off look like? It may mean allowing yourself to enjoy a summer picnic with friends – where they enjoy ice cream and you enjoy a slice of chilled watermelon – instead of telling your-self, "It's too hard! I'll get triggered by the ice cream if I go."

It may be enjoying some brown rice with your dinner, expanding your diet beyond the scope of protein and green vegetables. It may mean sitting with this meal to see, "Is it my beliefs and thoughts about rice (that it's a bad food or triggers a binge, for example) that lead me to overeat it? Or is it a food that my body truly reacts negatively to?"

It may be experimenting to see which fruits trigger sugar cravings and which don't; and does how much fruit make a difference? What about grains? Wheat? Whole wheat versus white? It means being willing to test, experiment, and potentially make mistakes. It means being willing to be a work in progress rather than a finished project.

The two tools for healing

In other words, it means being willing to really probe to uncover what is a true sugar addiction and what is an emotional dependency on food – something that abstinence will not fix.

You can see how scary this may feel, because it means being willing to look unfinished, to fail, to mess up, to be sloppy, to look worse before you look better.

This takes both trust and humility – caring more about your healing and inner freedom than looking foolish in the short term. It means trusting your ability to test and explore and listen to your body and discern the subtle difference between emotional overeating and overeating from a sugar reaction – and then knowing how to respond.

In the first case, the solution is probably not abstinence, but finding ways to soothe and meet your needs without food. In the second case, the solution is probably abstinence (if you want to minimize the sugar addiction cycle.)

Mix up the two, and it gets hard. It can lead to rigidity about food if you always approach overeating with abstinence.

On the other hand, if you *are* sugar sensitive and you continue to eat sugar, you will constantly be caught in the addictive sugar cycle. You may find it incredibly difficult to do the deeper inquiry of separating from food. This is why many of us who are sugar sensitive feel like such failures when we try to heal our overeating by following the advice of "eat everything in moderation."

How to find healthy abstinence

It's a tricky balance. There are some foods that may cause problems for you and that you may be better off abstaining from. You may be allergic to them (and we can crave and feel addicted to foods to which we have an allergy. Julia Ross's book *The Mood Cure* explores this in further detail.) You may be sensitive to certain foods, like sugar, that require your not eating them to be free from the addiction.

Honor these needs and limits.

I think it's helpful to look at food as a continuum versus abstinence or moderation (or good and bad.) There aren't bad foods - just foods that may not be great for your body!

There are some foods I eat every day, some I eat every now and then, and some I don't eat at all. In the not at all category is dried fruit, sugar and white flour. I do my best to abstain from these foods as they make me feel terrible. It's a choice to feel good, not a moral judgment.

In the every now and then category are grains and dairy. I don't eat these foods every day but I do eat - and enjoy - them. The reasons vary. In the case of dairy, eating dairy everyday gives me congestion, stomachaches and sinus headaches. In the case of grains, I don't eat them everyday as they give me stomachaches when I eat them daily.

In the category of every day are protein foods (meat, legumes, eggs, fish), nuts, oils and seeds, tons and tons of vegetables of all shapes and sizes and fruit. And yet within that container there are differences - I eat fruit in moderation - usually one to two servings or less a day. By contrast, I eat protein at every meal.

I feel better eating some carbohydrates. But too many carbohydrates - even whole, unprocessed carbs - are too much for my body and I crave sugar. Again, this is *my* experience as a woman with low blood sugar, depressive tendencies, and sugar sensitivity. So I eat what I consider a moderate carbohydrate diet. That is the balance that works for me. Too little carbs and I feel deprived. Too many carbs and I crave sugar.

It's taken me many years to get to this point. I ate too few carbs and felt deprived. Then I ate too many and craved sugar. But I kept experimenting and learning. It's part of the growth process, to be okay with being in process. You will go through this too. It's normal and okay. Let yourself grow and experiment and find your balance.

Later on in the chapter, I'll share what a typical meal looks like so you can see how this translates into an actual meal.

The good news is that as you experiment and tinker you find your center. You find what works for your body and you respond - not because of what an expert tells you but because you're listening to the wisdom of your body. This softens the anxiety about food dogma and allows you to trust what works for you.

How sugar abstinence and emotional inquiry work together

As you find your abstinence, at the same time, be very, very careful about overdoing this and putting all foods that you overeat in the "off limits" category. This is often a protective measure, a stalling tactic to avoid looking into why you overeat in the first place. You can choose abstinence as a way to avoid facing the deeper issues – of digging into your food stuff to uncover, "What is really going on here?"

Sugar abstinence gives you some freedom from the physical urge to eat and binge on sugar. It gives you more balance as your moods feel more stable without the sugar induced mood swings. It can improve your physical health.

But it doesn't give you emotional freedom from food. Emotional freedom comes from the inquiry work of understanding what is really going on when you seek food for comfort, solace, care, or nurturing.

The fruits of emotional freedom are many. They include:

1. Enjoyment of food instead of fearing it and seeing it as the enemy. You learn how to quiet your inner food cop, which is really about questioning all the thoughts and food rules you hold in your head about food. Gently, over time, these soften and release. What freedom.

2. Trusting yourself. You trust that you can be around sugar and not get triggered. You don't have to hide from life. You trust your innate ability to care for your body, mind and spirit. You know that you have an inner reservoir of strength and solace, where you have all the wisdom, courage, and discernment you need to walk your path with integrity.

You don't feel as fearful about slip ups or a time when you may go back to sugar. You may even welcome these – not that you invite them in with a, "What the hell! Let's binge!" approach – but you understand that every situation is a gift – an opportunity to open your heart and love. You know that going back to sugar would not be the end of the world, in the same way that gaining weight or losing a job or going through some other challenge would not be the end of the world.

3. Pleasure. Letting yourself eat a wide variety of non-sugar foods. Creating a food container that allows for your many needs and many different ways of eating.

4. Gratitude. You focus more on all the delicious foods you can eat and less on what you can't. You realize the abundance of foods that are yours for the tasting, the bounty of life's table. You feel content with "enough" and are not so attached to a "craving, wanting self" who is always looking for the next hit around the corner.

5. Acceptance. Learning to love the foods that love you back. Your taste buds and desires for food may change. You'll savor a chilled slice of watermelon on a hot summer day instead of pining for an ice cream sundae; strawberries and cream will taste more delicious than candy ever did; a hearty soup will fill your belly in the way that chocolate chip cookies once gave you warmth; comfort food will feel like a baked potato with butter instead of a bag of chips.

Choosing your path

In my experience, most people don't want to do the inquiry. They don't want emotional freedom. They just want the physical freedom because, let's face it, inquiry is scary. It means letting go of food stuff on a deeper level versus looking at sugar abstinence as a magic pill that solves all our food problems.

Do you have to do the emotional inquiry to be sugar free? No.

And yet I would gently encourage you to do both – to physically and emotionally unhook from sugar. I say this because this deep level of healing and acceptance is the only way I found joy and pleasure in food. It's the only way I found both inner and outer peace.

More than that, the emotional inquiry, while intense and painful at times, is also incredibly beautiful and healing. It's how I learned to love myself and stop all the self judgment, blame and self-hatred. It's how I found an inner sanctuary and rebuilt the relationship that I had with myself.

This was the deeper gift I found in exploring my food stuff. How could I not want the same gift for you?

Deprivation

As our cravings soften, and as we pay more attention to what's right here – the delicious food on our plate versus the candy in the jar – we find that place of enough. We find joy and satisfaction and pleasure in the bite we're eating instead of constantly seeking out the next moment – the next meal, the next bite, the foods we're not eating - to finally be enough.

When we focus on what's here, we feel okay. We can even feel more than okay – we can feel content. Dare I say, happy?

The real deprivation is not what is on our plate. Deprivation exists in the mind. We feel deprived when we tell ourselves, "I can't have that and it's not fair and I want it." We get wrapped up in what meditation teacher Tara Brach calls "the wanting self," and all our focus is on gimme, gimme, gimme.

We also feel deprived when we tell ourselves, "I have to protect myself from sugar at every corner. It's out to get me. I have to watch my back." We contract our life, making it smaller and smaller and smaller in our attempt to make it feel safer and safer and safer. Then we blame food for all our problems, when we're the ones who are saying, "No, you can't do that. Not that either. No, no, no. Stay away."

Letting go of control

The enemy is not outside of ourselves. It is not big, bad sugar. We get hooked when we believe the thoughts in our heads that are not true. Mindless thinking - which we all experience - has us contract in fear and control.

It's much easier to look at a birthday party and say, "They're going to be eating cake and ice cream. I can't go," then to ask ourselves, "Why am I desiring cake and ice cream in the first place? What emptiness do I feel inside that I am trying to meet with food? Why am I keeping myself from community, from something that would be joyful and fun, because I feel this urge to control and protect myself? What am I trying to avoid feeling by immediately jumping to, I can't go?"

We can put all the blame on sugar and focus all our efforts on keeping this bad, bad, bad thing out of our lives. We do this because it keeps us from having to face our own hurt. It's a classic defensive maneuver.

As long as we are staying focused on minimizing the sugar threat, we can avoid examining all the feelings and needs that drive our desire for sugar in the first place.

I'll say it again: Do you have to go so deep to stay sugar free?

For both inner and outer freedom from sugar, I'm going to say yes.

I know people who stay sugar free without doing this inner work. I also tried this approach myself.

Most people who follow this path are pretty miserable. They have all the "right" surface behaviors – they eat clean, whole foods; they've lost the extra weight; they don't eat any sugar – and yet they feel utterly joyless. "Is this all there is?" they write and ask me.

"I feel like something's still missing," they wonder. Of course something is still missing – they still feel separated from their deepest needs and feelings. They feel separate from life. They feel separate from others as they safeguard themselves against every possible danger.

We can even turn on others and label them as out to get us. We filter their behavior through the lens of, "They don't want me to be sugar free! They're out to get me! They're trying to get me to slip!" We create stories that aren't true and then we live them out.

We can turn arrogant. We've found a way to somehow escape the temptations that other people have to live through. (Poor souls.) And if we start to feel especially confident, we may try and tell these poor souls, "If you only ate like I did, and gave up sugar, all your problems would be solved, too." A wonder that they don't respond with enthusiasm.

Oh, beloved. Do you see how this path leads to suffering?

Do you see that it will not give us the peace we seek?

Do you see that giving up sugar is not about trying to somehow control or manage life's pain?

You may be reading this wondering, "Is she saying I shouldn't try to find a sugar abstinence?"

No. I'm not trying to discourage you from questioning your relationship to sugar. Rather, I'm suggesting that you sit and inquire into your motivations for wanting to give up sugar in the first place. I'm suggesting that if your motivation is coming from fear, control, and self-hatred, no matter how successful your sugar abstinence is on the surface, you won't have peace.

The only way to have both inner and outer peace from sugar is to do this from love.

Why we give up sugar

It gets to the very root of why we are doing this.

Understand what giving up sugar can and can't do for you. Yes, it can absolutely minimize a physiological drive for sugar. The analogy I use (and forgive me if it's getting tiring) is that abstaining from sugar turns off the switch to eat sugar (and then binge on sugar) in my brain. So, yes, staying off sugar was (and still is) very helpful for this reason. Once I stopped eating sugar, I wasn't always being pulled down the addictive pathway of one cookie followed by a trail of thousands of other goodies. It gave me a measure of freedom, a safe mental space where I didn't feel so hooked.

And yet one of the hardest lessons for me to learn about food and sugar was that sugar abstinence – by itself - was not enough. Sure, I'd read it before, in the tales of other people who had been addicted to food. But it wasn't until I'd lived it that I knew what they were talking about.

We can't escape life with abstinence. It, by itself, doesn't give us inner peace. Trying to control ourselves to never eat sugar again is not the solution. It can be abstinence, but it's not sobriety - inner peace about our choices; freedom from compulsion, and self-trust. This deeper sobriety is how we find joyful sugar free living.

What finally gave me lasting peace from sugar and overeating was by following this process. My next book will cover these steps in detail, but for now here's a summary of my journey:

1. Becoming sugar abstinent. This involved setting up daily self care structures and regular eating habits. Honoring my limits about foods that caused pain in my body. Accepting my biology and the limit of not eating sugar.

2. Awareness. Inquiring into my feelings. Observing myself – how was I using food? Why was I abusing it? What are the deeper issues? What are my patterns?

3. Honoring my needs and feelings. Being okay with being vulnerable and human and in process. Caring for my deeper needs and feelings without food.

4. Self soothing. Learning new patterns of soothing and comforting myself without food. Caring for my sensitivity. Moving energy and creating energetic boundaries instead of getting stuck and feeling overwhelmed by other people's feelings or energy.

5. Lowering expectations. Unhooking from my super high expectations about my body size and weight. Softening perfectionism and all or nothing thinking.

6. Creating internal sanctuary. Befriending myself and creating self trust. Creating mindfulness and awareness in my everyday life. Slowing down and paying attention. Turning inwards instead of outwards for soothing.

7. Detaching from my stories. Unhooking from the false belief that I'm flawed and worthless. Seeing that I'm much deeper than my behavior or "flaws." Unhooking from my habitual patterns and reactivity - how I react when I'm feeling scared, overwhelmed, anxious or not okay. (For me, that was either turning to food in bingeing or, alternatively, turning to dieting to be thinner and feel better about myself.) Finding space for a new way of being with my discomfort.

8. Unconditional acceptance. Turning towards my needs and feelings instead of running from pain. Caring for my feelings. Dropping judgment about how I "should" be or feel or how life should be. Finding compassion, lovingkindness and forgiveness for myself. Dropping blame. Opening my heart to everything - not seeing my sugar sensitivity or food problems as a punishment or judgment against me but as a gift to bring me home to self-love.

If you follow these steps, you'll see that sugar abstinence is only the first step of many. Look at your sugar abstinence as the beginning – not the end – of your journey. This step is crucial because you gain the mental space to uncover what is really going on. Without your sugar abstinence, you're too painfully caught in cravings and addiction to do the deep healing work.

 Once you have some space from that intense space of craving, you can work on changing your habit of turning to food, period. You can learn how to soothe your emotions, how to question your thoughts, how to unhook from negative thinking, and how to face and feel your feelings.

This process took me several *years*. As daunting as that may sound, the rewards are deep and many. My journey of unhooking from food – as painful as it was at times - was also incredible beautiful. I cried years of uncried tears, I finally faced emotions that I had been running from for most of my life, I found a deep, abiding love for myself that had long been missing.

I would gladly do it over because it brought me home to myself. What I most feel towards my food pain is gratitude. My journey broke my heart open, over and over and over again. The more I broke open, the freer I felt – and the less I feared food.

Flexibility with food as you heal

Throughout this growth process, your approach to food will change. I found that over time, as I healed the roots of my dependence on food, my food rules gradually softened. They went from a diet of primarily non-starchy vegetables and lean protein to a flexible food container that held a wide variety of foods – animal foods like meat, eggs, cheese, butter, kefir; plant foods like starchy vegetables, non-starchy vegetables, and greens; nuts, oils and seeds; low sugar fruits like apples and berries; gluten free grains like popcorn, millet, brown rice and quinoa; legumes like black beans and pinto beans and more.

I gained more flexibility and fluidity. I began to detect the subtle nuances of rhythm and ebb and flow. I noticed that I craved my heartiest meal at lunch time, while I wanted a lighter dinner and a medium sized breakfast. I noticed when I had too little carbs and too much; when I had too little protein and too much.

I observed how my desires for certain foods changed with the seasons, the time of day, and even based on my external circumstances. For example, when I moved, I craved grounding foods for several weeks. (Grounding foods include root veggies - potatoes, yams, and carrots - winter squashes, animal protein, and nuts.) It was as if my body knew it needed to feel more stable during a time of chaos.

I saw how subtle differences like traveling, being in a different part of the country, or even what kind of projects I was working on affected my desires for certain foods.

I noticed that eating some foods every day – dairy, in my case - made me feel congested or "heavy," and yet those same foods, when eaten every now and then, felt fine.

I had tremendous freedom to eat from a wide variety of foods – a very generous food container – even as there were many foods that were outside my food container that I didn't eat – things like sugar, dried fruit, and flour. This approach to food felt like something I could joyfully maintain over a lifetime, and this is the way I continue to eat today.

How your food container changes over time

I don't know if I could've eaten this way when I was first healing from sugar addiction. I may have been too triggered by my anxiety about eating carbs, fruit, or grains – foods I had labeled as "bad." My body may have needed a level of physical healing before I could tolerate foods with natural sugars, like fruit. I look back and realize that I probably needed that feeling of safety that really strict food rules gave me.

Today, I know that I can maintain my sugar abstinence within a broad food container. I feel like I can pick and choose from a wide variety of foods – without the danger of going back to sugar. The result of this is that I don't feel anxious about food. My inner food cop has quieted. I don't fear food as the enemy, but view it as something joyful that I can use to lovingly nourish myself. I take pleasure in food again.

Wisdom is knowing when to let go. Know when to expand your eating, loosen some of your food rules, and be willing to experiment and see – how does eating this way make me feel? Do I want a lighter dinner? A heavier breakfast? Can I eat fruit? How much? Does my body react differently to it when I eat it with some protein, like a handful of almonds?

Eat it, try it and listen to what your body says. You will experiment over and over again. Eating is a daily mindfulness exercise. We can fight this, or we can open to it.

I know that my food container, like my needs, will grow, change and ebb and flow. I am mindful of what I eat and pay attention to how eating a food makes me feel.

I also pay attention to my life itself. I may go through a period where I'm using food to heal. I think of a good friend who had stage 4 cancer and used his diet to support his healing. He had a very strict diet –

something he freely chose because he wanted to live. And yet that is what he needed. What you or I may need may be very different.

Where we get into trouble is when we hold rigidly to a certain way of eating. Okay, this is the way it has to be for life. Then, when our circumstances change, like when we aren't fighting off cancer, or when we aren't 25 anymore and our metabolism has changed, or when we are pregnant and needing to respond differently, we can actually resist changing because this is the way it's supposed to be. We resist the ebb and flow of change instead of responding to it.

Comparing ourselves to others

We also get stuck when we look at someone else's food container and say, "Because they eat that way, I need to eat that way too."

For women, we often do this when we try and emulate the way a celebrity or movie star eats. A movie star may have an incredibly focused way of eating – and a very disciplined approach to her body – because her ability to do her job is based primarily on what she looks like. The question is why we apply these same standards to ourselves.

Creating your food container may mean sitting with your desires and drives to uncover what really motivates your behavior.

For both men and women, I'd encourage you to spend some time in quiet reflection on this question: "How much of my drive to be in charge of my eating – beyond eating or not eating sugar - is not because of a sugar addiction but because of a desire to control my body and have it look a certain way?"

I say this very gently, and very kindly, because it is so common, particularly for women. So much of our desire to be in charge of food is because we want to be in charge of our bodies. We don't want to accept that we can't control everything and that our weight and our health is not entirely in our hands. We don't want to accept that our bodies will age and get old. We don't want to accept that our physical appearance will change.

Trying to be at our "best" weight

One of the reasons I struggled with food "stuff" for so long was because I always wanted to be at my thinnest possible healthy weight. My expectations were super high. Because of these high expectations, I was always trying to control my eating or eat the "best" way to be at my natural thinnest and "best" weight. So every meal was a gauntlet, every binge kept me from this magic spot and had to be controlled, every food had to be analyzed about whether it would keep me thin. I didn't eat to enjoy my food; I ate to achieve this goal of physical perfection. And yet I justified it because I wasn't trying to be as thin as I'd been when I had an eating disorder. I justified it because other women were doing the same thing.

It was a very miserable way to live. Because my expectations were so rigid, it was a full time job to fulfill them. And every slip was a huge crisis, because the goal was so elusive and so important.

Then I had this pesky habit of rebelling and feeling deprived and bingeing. I would get so pissy at myself and just furious at myself and my body for not cooperating in the way I wanted it to. I would beat it up and yell at it and tell myself, "Get your act together." I would tell myself things like, "You bad girl. You can't have any pretty clothes until you stop this and lose this extra weight!" like telling a child, "No dessert for you, you bad girl!" The only way I could have pleasure was by being "good."

When I got really quiet with this desire to be super fit and super thin, I realized how much of it was based on my fears of not being lovable and okay. I wanted to be the fittest, prettiest woman in the room. I wanted to be my ideal self – because if all my stuff was together, all my kinks ironed out, I thought I would finally feel good about myself. I thought I could finally quiet the fearful voice that told me, "You're not okay."

Body acceptance and eating

This is very different than eating to care for yourself and eating for health. My ego was still very much in charge. I was still trying to control. I was still fixated on my body. It was very challenging for me to soften this expectation and accept, "I may very well be 10 pounds heavier than what my mind thinks is ideal or what I would like to be." And I had to get to a point of, "Do I want to be perfect or do I want to be free?" I had to get to a point of loving myself in a way that wasn't attached to how I behaved or what I looked like.

I have given away most of my clothes from the super fit, super thin time and accepted that as a nearly 40 year old woman who has had 4 kids, and who is not willing to monitor every single bite of food she puts in her mouth, and who is not willing to kill herself with super intense workouts, that I probably won't ever wear that size again. And it is okay.

This is still an evolving process for me, and yet I see the tremendous freedom. I have moments of incredible tenderness and self-love, where I see myself through the eyes of love instead of through the eyes of judgment, blame and criticism. They are breathtaking in their beauty. Everything feels right in the world.

And then because I'm human, and because we're always continually facing our stuff, I forget, and the judgment creeps back in. I remember, I forget, I remember, I forget. I still have thoughts about, "But maybe if you did pay more attention to food you would lose 10 pounds?" and I am okay with that too. I try and sit with these thoughts and inquire, "What is this really about?" And it's usually about fear and being lovable and feeling okay. And I suppose I am okay with this, too, and am learning not to take this personally and judge myself for forgetting or for wanting life to be different. My job is not to control, but to pay attention and to inquire and do my best not to get hooked. To use everything as a way to open my heart and find the love that is there.

Sitting with your stuff

So sit with your stuff. As you gain some distance from the physical merry go round of sugar addiction, you're going to find some space. You're going to have the wherewithal to explore, "I wonder what this is about?" You will be given doorway after doorway after doorway to walk through – to learn, explore, uncover and grow.

You'll be able to discern – what motives are truly based on love and health and care, and which are based on my ego's desire to feel important and okay? And you'll face a point of decision of, "Do I want to follow my ego or do I want to have inner peace?"

You'll open the door a crack and then slam it shut. You may wish you'd never heard of me or sugar sensitivity. That's okay. Perhaps a little farther down the road you'll find yourself wondering, "What's behind that door?" And you'll open it again.

You'll explore, you'll retreat, you'll question, you'll cry, you'll laugh, you'll mourn, you'll experience the whole range of human feelings, all as you try and answer the question, "How do I create a joyful sugar free life? How do I love food and not feel driven by my desire for it at the same time?"

You ask the questions, and as Rilke wrote, "you live your way into the answers." Welcome, my friend, to the school of life.

Now I'm going to detach from this broad, skyline view on sugar, food and what to eat, and bring it down closer, to the ground floor level. The following suggestions are things that I've found helpful on the daily level as I think about food and what to eat.

Keep up your good habits.

Do you remember the foundation we built before you began your sugar abstinence? This included things like eating breakfast every day, eating regularly, eating protein, eating your meals while sitting down, and putting your food on a plate. In our sugar programs, we call this grounding. Grounding gives you a strong, rooted foundation from which to grow. Think of a tree planted in the ground, with deep roots, a thick, sturdy trunk, and flexible branches. With this strength, a tree grows tall, stretching upwards to the sky, bends with the wind and passing storms, and is a thing of beauty and shelter, as we rest under its branches.

It's the same for you. With a firm foundation, you give yourself the message, "I have what I need." When you have this inner reservoir of strength, you find that staying off of sugar is much easier – not something you have to force as much as something that you honor and follow. You bend with the storms of life without breaking. You have deep roots of nourishment.

You'll continue to ground yourself even as you continue your sugar abstinence. It's important to keep up with eating regular, healthy meals, because it's easy to let good habits slip, one at a time, until, before you know it, you're grazing in the kitchen, digging into the ice cream.

How does an ice cream binge happen, after a successful sugar abstinence? Well, you have a bit of ketchup and French fries here; a bagel one day; some Chinese take-out another (much Chinese food has sugar in it.) These little slips of sugar start to build, and coalesce until you give in to something bigger, such as ice cream, or a chocolate chip cookie out of the oven. Then, before you know it, you're eating sugar at every meal, wondering how you got there.

The way to prevent the slips is to stay grounded. Keep eating breakfast; eat protein with your meals; eat enough food so that you're satisfied. Your good habits are how you stay sugar free over the long term, not only how you become sugar free over the short term.

Self care is never done.

Self care is not something we do just once, like fixing a broken muffler, and poof! We're done. It's more akin to putting gas in our car, something we do over and over again.

One of the most frustrating things about being human is that we require upkeep. We have to make peace with our very tenderness – the fact that we regularly need to be fed, held, rested, loved, and nurtured. It's not something we can store up once, deplete, and then refill when we're on empty weeks or months later.

You may even find that your resistance to keeping up your foundation behaviors is due to your dislike of your human vulnerability. If you get quiet with yourself, you may find that you get really irritated at yourself when you get hungry; that you try and push yourself when you get tired instead of giving yourself a break; that you ignore the voice that says, "I'm done for the day" and prop yourself up with caffeine and sugar.

One of the core practices that I teach is to love and honor your humanity. We are so incredibly hard on ourselves. We often try and minimize our neediness – just the very word makes our skin crawl, it's so slimy and desperate and well, *needy*. I encourage you to look at your neediness as something natural and inherent to our human condition – not something to try and minimize.

Sit with your resistance and irritation when you start thinking things like, "I don't feel like making breakfast." Or, "I don't want to stop and take a break." "I shouldn't be hungry – I just ate a few hours ago!"

You'll see how our minds like to argue with reality – with our needs and feelings – and try and minimize them, argue with them, diminish them, or make us feel bad for having them!

It's the deeper work of exploring why we don't like taking care of ourselves, over and over again, day after day after day.

Eat whole foods. Drop the labels.

For a long time, I tried to put myself into a food camp. I wanted so much to belong to a tribe. I was a part of the low carb tribe, the Paleo tribe, the vegetarian tribe, the vegan tribe. I went from one tribe to another trying to find the "best" way to eat.

I was looking for belonging, and also safety – a way of eating that worked for my body. And yet once I aligned myself with a certain food camp I felt like a traitor when I disobeyed any of the rules. This caused a lot of anxiety and stress about being "bad-" something that would then create a desire to binge in order to soothe my anxiety.

So then I would leave the tribe and look for another – and feel a bit guilty and like an outsider until I'd found a new camp to join.

One day I realized that I was looking for something I really couldn't find –
an internal knowing about how to eat. I needed to stop looking for external
rules about how to eat and start listening to my body. I realized that there
were things I liked about each approach to food – and yet there were also
things I didn't like or that weren't a good fit for my body. I finally became
okay with a fruit salad approach of "a little of this" mixed with "a little of
that." This is called integrative nutrition – the idea that we integrate ideas
from many different camps to come up with a personal plan that fits our
needs.

Today, when people ask me how I eat, I reply, "A sugar free, primarily whole
foods diet." That's my integrative approach. It's an umbrella big enough to
encompass how I really eat and to allow for a lot of flexibility. It keeps me
from getting in debates about food dogma – something I personally don't
feel a need to explore. At the same time, I know that some people are really
passionate about a particular way of eating, and align themselves with a
food camp. That's okay, too.

Create balanced meals that are low on the GI index.

My meals are built around vegetables - both starchy and non-starchy veggies; some protein (primarily bison, venison – yes, my husband hunts -
poultry, wild Alaskan salmon, or legumes such as hummus, lentils, and
black beans), and some fat (olive oil, flaxseed oil, or butter, nuts or avocado.)

I add to this basic repertoire some fruit, plain kefir, and gluten free grains
like millet, quinoa or brown rice. (I suspect I have an allergy to gluten
which is why I rarely eat wheat, barley or oats.)

Another way of looking at food is to eat low on the Gylcemic Index. The
Glycemic Index measures how quickly carbohydrate foods turn into sugar
in the body. The higher the GI index, the faster the food is converted to
sugar. The lower the GI index, the slower the food is converted to sugar.
You want to eat low GI foods: these foods are naturally low in sugar and
won't raise your blood sugar. You can find more information about the

Glycemic Index on the web at www.glycemicindex.com, including the GI index of common foods.

Create food variety.

Nourishing yourself is not about eating raw salads all the time. There is a time for salads. And there will also be a time for denser foods, for heartier food, for celebratory food, for comforting food, for sharp thinking food, for healing food, for grounding food, for light food….and on and on.

There is a season for everything. Honor the shifting seasons. Your needs will change – throughout the day, if you're a woman, in your monthly cycle, throughout the seasons of the year, and throughout the seasons of your life.

When you're flexible and centered, you respond to these seasons, to these needs, to what is arising in you with appropriate nourishment. You drop the external shoulds that tell you, "You should eat blah, blah, blah" and you feed yourself what your body and spirit is calling for.

Include some fat in your diet.

I'll admit that this advice runs contrary to much of the conventional dietary wisdom. But I've found that I feel and look better - not to mention feeling more satisfied at mealtime - when I make sure I have sufficient fat in my diet. Sometimes I would crave sugar when I actually needed fat.

This doesn't mean that I eat rich desserts and cheese all day long. But at every meal or snack, I include a serving of fat: some nuts, avocado, guacamole, olive oil, butter, a small serving of cheese, or even some animal fat (such as the fat found in a bison burger, or a bit of chicken skin with my chicken.) When I eat fat, my nails and hair are stronger, thicker and shinier. I stay full, longer. My moods are better.

Be really careful with processed foods.

Sugar is in nearly every processed food, from salad dressing to ketchup.

Sugar free living means either making many foods from scratch, or, if you'd rather buy them, reading labels. It's important to read labels even if they're from the same company: sometimes one type of salsa will have sugar in it, and one won't, for example. I've found a few salad dressings that don't have sugar in them - I like the original Newman's Own vinaigrette - but we usually make our own as this is so simple.

As a general rule, our family generally doesn't eat a lot of processed foods. They are treat foods, a complement to a meal. We primarily shop the perimeter of the store, which means tons of fresh vegetables and fruit, some dairy, protein foods, and some staples.

We like making our own food. For example, our homemade black beans are much tastier than canned beans. This also effects how I eat. I find when I eat processed food I eat more. As the quality of the food decreases, I desire more quantity.

Accept that most modern foods aren't really food at all.

When you walk through a modern grocery store, you'll be bombarded by all sorts of packaged, processed, brightly colored, highly sugared, preserved, overly salted foods. When you think about what human beings have been eating over the millennia, you can see that we've only been eating this "junk" for a short period of time - primarily for the past sixty years.

Our bodies weren't designed to function optimally on junk. While, yes, it may taste good, and while, yes, it may be convenient, we trade taste and convenience for our very health. Most of the food in a modern supermarket isn't even food at all - but calorie laden, nutritionally empty junk that harms our bodies and disrupts our mood.

The food you eat has a profound effect on how you feel. How you fuel your body affects the functioning of all of your organs and systems, including your emotions, brain, and mental health. If you start to feel sorry for yourself because you can't/don't eat the typical American fare, recognize what that typical fare is: harmful to your body. A Diet Coke, a bag of potato chips, and a hot dog don't give your body the nutrients, vitamins, and minerals that it needs. But a glass of water, sliced strawberries, a raw vegetable salad, some brown rice, and a grilled chicken breast: this meal is full of antioxidants, vitamins, minerals, and protein that your body can use to function at its best.

Eat organic when possible.

I buy as much organic food as my budget allows. From a purely selfish point of view, it usually tastes better.

This means that our family spends a large portion of our budget on food. It can be a financial sacrifice, but the rewards are many: we're healthier, we need less doctoring, we have stronger immune systems, we help the environment, and we're not exposed to as many pesticides, antibiotics, and growth hormones.

It's a choice we're willing to make, and yet, like you, we've had many financial ups and downs that mean making hard choices about what we buy. I simply do the best I can. When I can buy more organic vegetables I do; when I have to settle for conventional vegetables I buy conventional vegetables. I try not to stress over it and I wash the produce really well.

Find ways to eat economically while eating more whole foods.

I concentrate most of our family's food dollars on organic meat and dairy products. This is for two reasons: first, I don't want my family exposed to the antibiotics and hormones in non-organic raised meat. These hormones accumulate in the fat of an animal, so it makes sense to buy organic butter or cheese. Also, I want to ensure that the meat I buy is from animals that were raised humanely. While I consciously choose to eat animal products, I don't want them to unnecessarily suffer from my decision to do so.

Then, as my budget allows, I buy other organic foods, such as fruits and vegetables and then beans and grains. I buy most of my beans, nuts and grains in bulk and save money this way.

There are several tricks you can use to save money while buying organic. Trader Joe's sells artisan and organic foods at incredible prices, and Costco is carrying more and more organic products. Co-ops can be great, as well, especially if you buy foods in bulk.

Look into butchering your own animal or eating game. My husband hunts so most of our meat is wild game. (As a beef raised Midwestern girl, it did take some time for me to adjust to the taste of game. I know it's not for everyone.) My husband shot a bison that we had butchered by our local butcher shop, filling our freezer with meat for over a year. With the cost of the animal and the butchering, we paid less than $4 a pound for grass fed, organic bison - compared to $5-$20 for the same bison in the grocery store. Granted, we live in Montana, where there are many bison ranches and abundant hunting, but you may be surprised at what you can find in your part of the country. A good place to start would be your local farmer's market: ask for local ranches or farms that allow you to buy a whole animal. We have several friends who will go in together to split a grass raised pig or cow.

Try flourless, sprouted breads.

For those of you who are sensitive to flour, you may want to try sprouted, flourless bread by Food for Life. (Go to www.foodforlife.com for more information.) Their products are sold in most health food stores in the freezer section, and I've even seen them in mainstream grocery stores. I ate their bread, English muffins, and tortillas for years without sugar cravings. Unfortunately, now I have a wheat and gluten sensitivity, so I don't enjoy them as I used to. But many people who had trouble with even whole wheat bread find that they do fine on flourless bread.

These products have a rich, nutty taste. They are quite filling and hearty. Sprouted breads are high in protein and low on the glycemic index.

Be careful with fruit.

While there are some nutritionists, doctors and health experts who say that you can never eat too much fruit, if you're sugar sensitive, eating an unlimited amount of fruit every day may trigger sugar cravings. While, yes, fruit has all sorts of vitamins and antioxidants that, say, are missing from a jelly donut, fruit is still very sweet. If I eat too much fruit, it triggers my sugar cravings, and can even give me a sugar rush. So I limit my fruit to primarily low sugar fruits - things like berries and apples versus grapes and pineapple. I also limit how much fruit I eat. I have at most one to two servings a day; more in the summer, less in the winter. I avoid dried fruit, because it's high sugar content makes it very addictive: a serving of raisins has more sugar than a candy bar, even if it's a "natural" sugar. In fact, raisins are my favorite binge food because the sugar hit is so strong.

I typically eat fruit with some protein – like a sliced apple with almonds or berries with plain kefir and almonds.

See how you feel on grains.

I don't eat grains everyday, as too many grains make me feel bloated and constipated. I prefer to eat non-starchy vegetables, starchy vegetables, and legumes as the filler in my meals. When I do eat grains, I choose mainly millet, quinoa, and long grain brown rice as the gluten grains (wheat, oats, barley and rye) feel terrible in my body.

There are some doctors who recommend abstaining from grains as a whole if you are sugar sensitive. This is where you can run experiments on yourself, to see how you feel after eating grains: Do you feel sleepy after eating grains? Do you feel bloated or gassy? Do you feel heavy? Do grains satisfy you? Does portion size matter: can you handle a small side dish of a grain, whereas a main course (such as a bowl of pasta) leaves you sleepy? Go a few days without eating grains, and see how you feel. Then add them back in your diet and see how your body reacts.

Watch out for hidden sugars.

Metabolically, there isn't much difference between a candy bar and a bowl of mashed potatoes: both are quickly turned into sugar in the body. This is why many sugar addicts may not overeat sugar as much as they overeat starchy foods, like potato chips, pretzels, cereal, or bread. These are hidden sugars: they don't look like sugar on the surface, and yet our bodies treat them as sugar.

I'm very careful with foods like tortilla chips and potato chips. For a long time I tried to permanently abstain. Today, I'm more relaxed about eating these foods. They aren't foods I eat every day or even every week. But I do eat them every now and then, making sure that I'm eating them with other food, and that I focus on eating a serving. I'm careful and cautious but I'm not 100% restrictive of them. This is different than how I first approached these foods.

When I really sit with my desire for these foods, I often find that I can make a healthier, whole foods version of them that tastes better. I make oven roasted potato fries, where I chop up potatoes (leaving the skin on, for the fiber) toss them with sea salt and olive oil and bake them in the oven on a cookie sheet. These taste better to me than regular French fries or potato chips.

So sometimes it's not about saying "no, I can't have that food" but getting creative and making a healthier version of it.

Proceed cautiously with Asian cuisines, such as Chinese or Thai food.

Nearly all Thai and Chinese dishes have sugar in them, and are very sweet. While you can make your own Thai or Chinese food and omit the sugar, be really cautious when eating out. Ask if you can have your meal made without sugar, or if they can make up a special meal just for you. Most restaurants are happy to comply.

Think twice about sugar substitutes.

Aspartame, Splenda, Nutrasweet, low carb "sugar free" treats: I know these foods seem like "freebies" - a way to be sugar free but still satisfy your taste buds. But in my experience, while they may not raise your blood sugar like their sugary counterparts, they still give your body the sweet hit that it's craving. This fuels a desire for more sweet foods, and can easily lead to a sugar binge. That craving, that desire for sweets, is what we're trying to free you from in the first place. Sipping Diet Coke all day long won't give you that relief.

Learn how to make your own.

For many processed foods that have sugar in them – like barbeque sauce, teriyaki or asian sauces, and spaghetti sauce – you can try learning how to make your own.

Over the years I've made sugar free versions of foods that typically have sugar in them. I've made my own barbeque sauce, Chinese, and spaghetti sauce. I've whipped up sugar free salad dressings, pizza sauce, and ketchup (although my children weren't thrilled by that particular experiment.)

My kids and I make homemade popsicles for snacks in the summer by making a protein fruit smoothie (bananas, berries, water and protein powder) and then freezing them in plastic popsicle molds.

While sugar free living may limit your intake of processed foods, my examples show that, most often, you can make your own sugar free versions. This is where creativity trumps convenience. It does take more time on your part, and that's something for you to decide if it's worth it or not.

If you're not into making your own – and that's perfectly okay - you can look for sugar free versions of these products at health food stores. When I was a young mother and wasn't working, I cooked a lot more. Now that life is fuller, I cook less and either buy premade sugar free versions or find an alternative – like salsa instead of ketchup.

Drink lots and lots of water.

I primarily drink water. I noticed that I often craved food – fruit in particular – when I was, in fact, thirsty.

I also drink unsweetened herbal tea, particularly in the winter. I rarely drink alcohol. I always preferred the sugar in food to the sugar in a glass of wine.

Many people who struggle with sugar sensitivity notice a family history of alcoholism, obesity or sugar sensitivity. Many people who are sensitive to sugar have had a previous problem with alcohol. If you suspect that drinking alcohol affects your sugar intake, please explore this with professional help.

I don't drink juice, although I serve my children watered down juice as a treat. They drink mostly water, too. If you're used to drinking sodas or other highly sweetened drinks, water will probably taste really bland to you. But that will change over time. (In college, I drank six 20 oz. bottles of Diet Coke….a day. Water tasted terrible at first, but soon, I craved it.) Try flavoring your water with a lemon or lime slice or a sprig of fresh mint to make it more palatable.

People have often asked me about milk. I haven't drunk milk in years due to allergies and lactose intolerance. I do drink unsweetened almond milk on occasion and will add it to smoothies.

Eat seasonally.

In fall and winter I rely on lots of hearty soups. I eat more seasonal vegetables, including winter squashes and more fat: nuts, guacamole, butter, olive oil, and flaxseed oil. I also opt for more warm or cooked vegetable dishes than raw salads. I eat less fruit in the winter, a serving a day or less.

In the summer, I eat more fruit, but stick mainly to berries and other low sugar fruits. I eat lots and lots of raw veggies as the warm days make me crave lighter, more water based foods. I don't require as much fat or heavy foods in the summer, either.

You're not the family garbage disposal.

My girlfriends and I jokingly call ourselves compost Moms as we finish off our children's leftovers after meals. We know we shouldn't do this, and yet we can't help ourselves, especially if our children are eating something that's not in our best interest, like macaroni and cheese. I know it feels wasteful, but it is not your job to finish your children's food. If you make pasta and no one likes it, you don't have to finish it off. You can throw it away.

I know it's hard to throw food away. I hate it: it feels like money down the drain. But sometimes your family won't like your dinner. Your kids don't finish their meal. You may serve yourself something that turns out to be too much food.

Your body is not the family garbage disposal. You can throw the food out. You can wrap it up and save it for the next day. You can feed it to the dog. Leftovers are not your personal responsibility. Here's another way to look at it. What's more important: saving the $4 worth of pasta, or preserving your mental health?

Restaurants are there to serve.
Ask for what you want.

There's a scene in *When Harry Met Sally* when Sally is ordering at the diner, and goes on for several minutes specifying exactly how she wants her meal served. The waitress is visibly annoyed; the audience laughs at her neuroticism.

I know it can feel awkward inquiring whether a recipe has sugar in it, or making up your own meal. But this is an opportunity where you can gently ask for what you need, without feeling a need to defend yourself. (It took me many years to get comfortable with this, so if it feels awkward at first, that's perfectly normal.)

If you had a food allergy, you wouldn't feel awkward questioning the ingredients in menu items. Give your sugar sensitivity the same courtesy. I ask for salads without croutons, sugar free salad dressings, and to have them omit dried fruit, a sweetened sauce, and candied nuts from my entree.

You can make your server your ally with a simple question like, "I don't eat sugar. Can you suggest something on the menu that's made without any added sugar?" Restaurants are becoming more accommodating to people with various dietary needs, and most are happy to comply.

Be careful with fast food.

I don't eat fast food, and haven't in years. Fast food made me feel icky and almost always contains sugar.

Instead, I take food with me when I'm spending a day doing errands. I pack some snacks like an apple and almonds, some diced chicken, chopped vegetables and raw cashews. If I do go out to eat for a quick meal, I stop by our local health food co-op, whose deli is fabulous. I can get a wonderful, healthy lunch of a big salad, some protein, and a few vegetable sides for a few dollars more than a fast food meal.

I rarely eat in chain restaurants. Much of the food in chain restaurants isn't cooked as much as it is reheated, and it often has sugar and preservatives in it. When I do go out to eat, I prefer to eat in local restaurants, especially those that feature local food.

One of my favorite ways to eat out is by having potlucks with friends. You get connection, community and delicious food, all in one. I'm always inspired by the dishes my friends make and I get to try new foods that I don't cook at home. I also get the "eating out" feeling without spending a lot of money. Usually I want to go out to eat because I'm tired of my cooking and I want some variety. Potlucks meet both needs without a huge investment.

Does this mean that I never, ever eat at a chain restaurant? Of course not. Sometimes life intervenes, like when I'm traveling with my daughter's soccer team and we all go out to eat in a large group at Chili's. Then, like anything in life, I simply try to do the best I can with the options I have available.

Snack smart.

But what if you're a busy family, with lots of activities that keep

you constantly in the car? Be proactive. Stash your car with a mini cooler (I've seen small ones that will actually plug into your cigarette lighter; how cool is that?) and a snack bag. Keep things like water bottles, bags of nuts (cashews, peanuts, almonds, and pistachios); string cheeses, fruit, sliced veggies, sandwich halves, and wraps (my children love sprouted tortillas filled with cheese, sliced meat, and hummus or guacamole) handy for those times when you're running from one activity to another, and your children – or you – need to be fed.

Plan ahead, prepare and do the best you can.

Think outside the box with breakfast foods.

One of the most popular questions I get is, "What do I eat for breakfast when I give up sugar?" It's true: most traditional breakfast foods are high in sugar.

I encourage you to think outside of the box. Most of my breakfasts are left-overs from the dinner I cooked the night before. So I have breakfasts like grilled salmon and veggies; black beans, salsa and sautéed kale; lentil soup; an egg frittata with lots of vegetables (I'm not a big egg fan so I need a large vegetable to egg ratio); steamed, buttered broccoli with grilled chicken and some red potatoes.

In the summer I may make a smoothie with unsweetened protein powder, flaxseed, coconut milk, and a few frozen strawberries. (I prefer something warm for breakfast in the winter.) I occasionally have plain kefir, raw almonds and flaxseed for breakfast.

My children have scrambled eggs in corn tortillas with salsa and cheese, steel cut oats with peanut butter toast (made out of sprouted bread), and protein smoothies with a side of rice cakes topped with cream cheese, peanut butter and no-sugar fruit spread. (I know this sounds gross, but my children love them.)

Keep your home stocked with sugar free foods.

It's important to keep up your habit of filling your fridge, freezer and pantry with healthy, whole, sugar free foods. It's easy to slip back into old routines, to buy ice cream "for the kids" or cookies "for your husband." But be honest: are you buying the goodies for them, or so that you can sneak a bite?

It's also important to have healthy foods in the house you can eat. Otherwise, you'll eat junk food because it's all that's there.

I'm kind to myself by buying healthy convenience foods as my budget allows, so I have quick, easy meals on hand for busy evenings. This may be a bag of frozen vegetables that I can add to some meat for a quick soup, individual packs of frozen salmon I can defrost for an easy dinner, or a rotisserie chicken from the deli.

I also like to keep sugar free treat foods in the house so I have dessert options. I enjoy popcorn popped on the stove with butter, macadamia nut butter, and greek style yogurt with almonds. Even though I don't eat these foods everyday, they add so much pleasure to my life and soften feelings of deprivation.

Change your shopping routines.

If you typically loaded up your shopping cart with lots of sugary, processed foods, you may need to switch up your shopping routine so that you aren't tempted to add those old familiar favorites into your cart. I remember a time when I always added a bag of candy to my purchases. When I first stopped eating sugar, I couldn't even walk down the candy aisle, I was so tempted to toss in a bag of Tootsie Rolls or Twizzlers. Over time, the desire lessened, and I was able to walk down aisles that had sugary foods without being overly tempted.

You may also change where you shop, choosing to buy more of your food from health food stores such as Whole Foods, Trader Joe's, or a local co-op. These stores offer lots of healthy, sugar free fare, are often beautifully laid out, and have staff that can help you find what you need. You may also enjoy shopping in farmer's markets in warmer weather, particularly as your intake of fresh fruits and vegetables increases. There's nothing that quite tastes like a carrot straight out of the ground, or a tomato off the vine.

I shop at several places for my food. In the summer, I shop my local farmer's markets as well as subscribe to a local CSA, a small farm where you get a share of vegetables.

Much of our meat comes from my husband's hunting, but I supplement that with organic chicken from Costco and some fish from the co-op.

I buy local farm eggs from my local health food store. I shop at several different health food stores and a co-op. I do bulk orders from Azure Standard (www.azurestandard.com), a fantastic health food co-op that comes once a month. (I would seek them out if you live in the delivery area, which encompasses most of the Western and Midwestern parts of the U.S.)

Costco is starting to carry more natural and organic foods, although you still have to read the labels: even many natural brands will add sweeteners to their foods. Costco is a buy for nuts, organic vegetables, organic peanut butter, organic chicken, organic butter, and organic salad greens.

Make food prep easy.

Eating mostly whole foods does mean spending more time prepping, cooking and shopping for food. This can be a significant time investment. I resolve this by cooking very simply. In the winter, this means lots of soups. Dinner may be as simple as creamy millet with sautéed vegetables, black beans and a salad.

I cook in bulk – making extras of whatever I'm making. It's easy to pop a bunch of red potatoes in the oven and bake them together. Then I can add them to several meals or eat them for snacks. I cook a big pot of black beans that we use for several days of meals. When I make a salad, I make it large enough to last for two or three days. I make enough tuna salad to last for a few days. I bake yams in a huge baking pan and eat them for more than one meal.

My husband cooks, too, and his meals are more complicated. It's an enjoyable activity for him, whereas after over a dozen years of cooking 3 meals a day, I'm less motivated to play with cooking. Another way I support and treat myself (depending on my income and food budget) is by buying pre-cooked, whole foods from my co-op's deli.

I tend to fix meals that come together quickly, and make large portions. Then, we have leftovers for the next day, which I usually eat for breakfast; my family, for lunch. My crock pot saves me hours of time, and is an easy way to cook healthy meals. I also have a Vita-Mix, a high powered blender that we use for making smoothies, slushies in the summertime, and hummus. I also encourage my children to be self-sufficient; as they get older, they help with cooking.

You may eat differently when you first go off sugar than after you've been sugar abstinent.

When I first went off sugar, I ate a more strict, low sugar diet. I didn't even eat much fruit or starchy vegetables. This felt good initially. But over time I wanted more variety. The meat and veggies didn't feel as good. My body had this sense that something was missing and I felt overloaded on protein.

When I learned more about nutrition and candida, I recognized that this was probably due to the candida in my body. Candida is a yeast that naturally resides in the body. An overgrowth of candida can lead to many symptoms that sound much like sugar addiction – intense cravings for sweets, lethargy, fatigue and more.

If you've had a longstanding issue with sugar, it's highly possible you may have an overgrowth of candida. Sugar feeds the candida. As the candida grows, it wants to be fed with more sugar.

As we reduce our sugar intake and boost our immune system, the excess candida becomes normalized. This is how this can feel in the body: When I went through my candida die off, my insatiable cravings for bread or sugar diminished. I felt super tired as my body healed. That instant, powerful hunger from the candida gave way to my own natural, building hunger. I no longer felt physically as out of control around food. (There were still my own internal anxieties that fed my overeating, but the physical drive to eat sugar softened.)

Because any sugar feeds candida – and this includes the natural sugars in fruit – this may explain why I didn't feel very good eating fruit when I first went off sugar.

Now that I've been sugar free for several years, I can choose to eat fruit in moderation (usually a serving a day) without the negative side effects. Again, this may be due to having normalized candida levels, as well as from stabilizing my blood sugar.

When I do notice that I feel light headed or have sugar cravings after eating fruit, I pay attention and listen to my body and back down. It's an ebb and flow I honor.

Extra help for parties, holidays, and other special occasions:

Parties, holidays, family gatherings: these are often sticky times for sugar abstinence. After all, sugar is usually the main star of the show: pumpkin pie on Thanksgiving; ice cream on the 4th of July; cookies at Christmas-time. Here's what helped me:

1. Focus on the company at parties, not the food.

For me, the real joy of parties and holidays is connecting with friends and loved ones. While food may be a part of the celebration, it's a side bonus, not the main course.

This wasn't always the case. For years, I eagerly anticipated parties - for the food, not the people. If you're like me, and typically treated holidays and parties as free-for-alls, times when all your normal rules of eating went out the window, you'll need to consciously change this mindset so that you aren't tempted to sink into old habits.

I focus on the people by playing games, talking with my friends and family, and playing with my children instead of hanging around the snacks. I also try to confine my eating to meal times - eating Thanksgiving dinner, for example, and not Thanksgiving dinner along with two hours of appetizers beforehand. If it's a cocktail party, I spend my time circulating among the guests, rather than hovering over the food table. I also eat a small snack or meal beforehand, so I'm not starving when I show up at a party. It's also okay to enjoy a party without participating in a meal.

2. Don't make a big deal out of the sugar.

Sometimes, the easiest way to opt out of a sugary dessert or other food is to simply say, "No, thank you." You don't need to offer a long winded explanation of your sugar abstinence.

You also don't need to eat the sugar just to please your hostess or grandma. If people insist, and keep pushing something sweet on you, just smile, and keep saying, "No." Most hostesses are not trying to sabotage your eating plan but simply want to ensure that you've had enough to eat and that you're enjoying yourself. After all, every hostess wants her party or dinner to be a hit; this includes a full, satisfied belly on every guest. So if a hostess is insistent, don't take it personally: she just wants a happy guest.

You don't have to defend yourself or attack her. Just keep gently saying, "No."

3. At the same time, stay firm.

Sometimes, you do need to offer more than a simple, "No." You may be pestered until you want to give in. This is when you may want to offer an explanation, such as, "I don't eat sugar. I'm really good with just tea. Thank you."

4. Bring something that you can eat.

I always make sure that the dish I contribute to potlucks, barbeques, and family get togethers is something that I can eat. In other words, I don't volunteer to bring dessert. That way, even if the meal is something that I can't eat, like a sugar laden ham, I'll have a dish that I can enjoy. Even if you weren't told to bring anything, you can always bring an appetizer: again, make it something that you can eat, like veggies and hummus, not a heaping plate of nachos. This can stave off your hunger if your hostess serves lasagna with garlic bread and chocolate cake.

5. State your preferences beforehand.

Many considerate hostesses will inquire about any food allergies or preferences beforehand. Use this opportunity to express that you don't eat any refined sugar, and suggest a main course that you can eat.

6. Bring a non-sugar dessert.

We used to host a 4th of July bash in our backyard. We supplied the meat, and our friends and neighbors brought side dishes, appetizers and desserts. Guests always brought a slew of cookies and brownies, and yet they went untouched once we bring out a huge watermelon for cutting. Think of non-sugary dessert options that you can add to parties and celebrations - such as a fruit salad, berries with cream, or a melon. People often prefer these to richer fare.

Focus on what you can eat.

It's easy to start to feel sorry for yourself, when you think of all of the foods that other people get to eat - things like donuts and ice cream - that you don't. This is part of the grieving process.

Over time you'll focus less on what's missing and more on what you have

- all of the wonderful foods you do get to eat. All those yummy fruits and vegetables; steak, a good burger, chicken on the grill: those foods are worth celebrating, too. By switching your attention to what you can eat, versus what you can't, you feel grateful rather than resentful. A grateful heart is more likely to resist the call of donuts, whereas a resentful heart is always focused on "getting even" - which usually involves a sugar binge.

It's actually easier than you think.

After reading my suggestions about what I eat, you may be feeling discouraged. You may think there's *no* way you can eat this way; that there are too many restrictions. A few gentle reminders: first, it's taken me over ten years to get to this point. I didn't eliminate all of these foods or start eating so many whole foods overnight.

It was a gradual learning process, a gradual changing of my taste buds, a gradual weaning of junk foods that made my body feel terrible. So give yourself time. Let yourself grow into your changes instead of expecting yourself to make them overnight.

I'll also remind you that I'm extremely sugar sensitive. We're all different. You may be able to handle foods that my body doesn't handle well, such as more fruit, or more whole grains. On a scale of 1 to 10, I'm pretty extreme in my sugar sensitivity: I'm a 9 or a 10. You may be a 1 or a 2, by contrast.

It's also important to remember that when you eliminate sugar from your diet, your taste buds change. Your physical cravings for sugar will lessen. You'll start to crave more fresh, whole foods when you start to feel the difference of eating this way.

Lastly, understand that I willingly make these sacrifices. There's no one forcing me to eat this way. While I am disciplined in my sugar abstinence, I do it with joy. Most of the time, I don't call attention to the way I eat. I simply do it.

Eating this way makes me feel good. I feel balanced. I feel whole. I have abundant energy, stable moods, and I maintain a healthy weight. When

I don't eat this way, I suffer on so many levels: psychologically, mentally, physically, spiritually. So the pain of eating sugar outweighs the pleasure for me.

Over time, as sugar free living becomes the norm, you'll find your taste buds changing. It's as if sugar dulled your taste buds, and now, without the sweet foods in your life, your tastes are reawakening. You'll taste the natural sweetness in foods like meat, nuts, carrots, and peas.

You'll have a bowl of juicy strawberries, and they will taste deliciously sweet - like the strawberry flavored candy you used to eat. Likewise, if you previously relied on lots of salty, processed food, your taste buds will gradually taste the natural flavors of foods, without the chemicals and excess seasoning. It will get to the point when foods with sugar taste too sweet to you, or processed foods taste too salty.

What snacks may look like:

So what do I eat for snacks? What snacks do I give my kids? I tend to eat 4 meals a day. I don't snack as much as I eat smaller, frequently spaced meals. If I have a snack, they're usually almonds, raw cashews, pistachios, pecans or my favorite – a sliced green apple with almonds.

Here are snack ideas from my family's repertoire:

1. toast with peanut butter

2. string cheese

3. cheese and whole grain crackers

4. baby carrots

5. guacamole and veggies

6. hummus and veggies

7. corn tortillas with hot melted cheddar cheese (We put several on a cookie sheet and stick them in the broiler until the cheese is melted and bubbly.)

8. a serving of fruit, such as an apple, some grapes, some berries, or a nectarine

9. an apple or banana, cut into slices, with almond butter or peanut butter

10. winter squash with cinnamon, pecans and butter

11. plain yogurt with almonds and berries (we use fresh when available; frozen in the winter)

12. a rice cake with cream cheese and peanut butter, sometimes with a dash of a no-sugar added jam

13. sugar snap peas

14. a sprouted, whole grain wrap filled with a mix of veggies, cheese, and protein (such as diced chicken or turkey)

15. a baked potato with butter and grated cheddar cheese (This is one of my children's favorite after school snacks.)

16. nuts: almonds, cashews and pistachios are our favorites

17. smoothies - we probably make a smoothie 4-5 times a week. We use a variety of frozen fruits, protein powder, bananas, plain yogurt and water. The children love them! In the summertime, we also pour our smoothies into plastic popsicle molds and make our own healthy popsicles.

18. veggies with ranch dressing (You can find some ranches that don't have sugar in them, but be careful, and read the labels.)

19. an antipasto platter of olives, sliced mozzarella cheese, tomatoes, and grapes

20. a corn tortilla filled with warmed refried beans, cheese, and a dash of salsa

21. a hard boiled egg

22. air popped popcorn with butter and sea salt

23. a tuna or chicken salad sandwich

24. a piece of leftover quiche from breakfast

25. black beans with grated cheese and salsa

I find it helpful to treat snack time as a normal meal, just with smaller portions. So give your children half a turkey sandwich, for example, or a small cup of the soup you made for dinner. One trick I also use is setting out a bunch of cut up veggies (such as red peppers, carrots, tomatoes, celery, and cucumbers) while I make dinner. My children willingly eat the veggies because they're hungry, and I don't worry about them filling up on junk right before dinnertime.

What meals may look like:

I tend to eat the same kinds of food at each meal; in other words, I don't eat different foods for breakfast or lunch than I do at dinnertime.

If you could deconstruct my typical plate, it would look like this: at least ½ of the plate would be filled with vegetables. This may include a raw salad, cooked veggies, and some starchy veggies. ¼ of the plate is filler – brown rice, legumes, millet, or more starchy veggies. ¼ of the plate is then protein such as salmon, chicken, turkey, bison, or legumes.

The fat comes from olive or flaxseed oil on the salad dressing, or butter on the veggies, or the natural fat in the meat.

That's it. If I'm filling hungrier, I may add more filler or protein. If I want a lighter meal, I have more veggies and less meat or legumes.

I'll offer a list of sample meals from my own life, including some of my favorites:

1. Grilled chicken with grilled veggies, a big raw vegetable salad and potatoes

2. Chicken Caesar salad (without any croutons)

3. Roast chicken with green beans in butter, salad, and roasted potato fries

4. A giant taco salad with guacamole, salsa, black beans, a huge bowl of salad greens, sautéed onions and peppers

5. Lentil soup with a large side salad

6. Roast turkey with roasted acorn squash, salad, and steamed broccoli with butter

7. Roast beef with tomatoes, onions, and carrots and sautéed squash (zucchini or yellow squash)

8. Quiche, but without the crust

9. Grilled salmon, stir fry veggies, and brown rice

10. Chicken salad with mayo and veggies on a huge green salad

11. Chili with pinto beans, peppers, tomatoes and onions with a huge green salad

12. Bison steak, sautéed mushrooms, guacamole, a huge raw vegetable salad

13. Chicken, black beans, salsa, guacamole, jicama, peppers, onions, tomatoes and garlic on a huge salad

14. A brothy soup with lots of vegetables and protein, such as diced chicken or black beans

15. A clean out the fridge soup with whatever veggies I have, some potatoes, and either black or pinto beans

16. An egg frittata with lots of sautéed veggies, eggs, and a topping of parmesan cheese

17. Roast chicken thighs with olives, onions, garlic, diced tomatoes, and mushrooms; a large side salad

18. Hamburgers (without a bun) with sautéed mushrooms, onions, lettuce, cheese and tomato, a side salad, and a few homemade fries (I slice potatoes into thin strips, sprinkle them with salt and olive oil, and bake them in the oven.)

19. My comfort food meal: creamy millet with sautéed veggies like kale, onions, peppers, mushrooms, and tomatoes

20. A light summer meal: green beans steamed with butter, a large raw salad with radishes, tomatoes, peppers, cabbage, greens, and cucumbers topped with black beans

6

STAYING SUGAR FREE FOR LIFE

In the next phase, you're moving from your first few weeks of sugar abstinence to maintaining your sugar abstinence over the long haul. This takes a different focus than your sugar detox. While your sugar detox was often physically challenging, you were able to focus and get through it, knowing that the discomfort was only for a time.

But now you're facing years without sugar, not a few days or a week. This entails an examination of why you ate sugar in the first place, and the function that sugar served in your life. In order to be sugar free for life, you'll need to find ways to meet these needs without sugar - a journey that you're really just beginning.

Why Did You Abuse Sugar In The First Place?

While the first two weeks without sugar can be physically challenging, this challenge is ameliorated by high motivation and enthusiasm. It is in the following weeks and months, as your enthusiasm wanes, when it's easiest to slip up and eat sugar.

Often this occurs because we're human and we forget. We feel good and forget just how awful eating sugar made us feel. We think that because we're not craving sugar and are out of the addiction cycle that we can eat a bite or a small serving and be fine.

We need to replace our old thinking with new thinking. We need to remind ourselves that we've made a lifestyle change and create the structures to support it.

In many ways, giving up sugar is just the beginning. What you've accomplished in your sugar detox is eliminated your body's physical, chemical dependence on sugar. Staying sugar free, however, means eliminating your *emotional* dependence on sugar: examining why and how you turned to sugar in the first place.

If you used sugar as a way of easing your anxiety, anger, sadness, loneliness, or frustration, sugar abstinence won't solve this.

In that respect, the next few months may be the most challenging as you examine the ways you used sugar for comfort or protection. If you subconsciously used sugar to feel safe, or to avoid pain, healing your sugar addiction may force you to confront these feelings. You may notice buried dreams arise, feeling fearful of the opportunities that now await you. (Sometimes we get more comfortable living in pain than living unencumbered.) You may feel overwhelmed by intense feelings that are no longer numbed by food.

I want to encourage you that you're strong enough to handle your feelings in this normal, natural - and also uncomfortable - stage of growth.

Our fear of facing our feelings can keep us fixated on abstinence as the solution to all our food problems. And yet when we don't address the underlying roots of our sugar addiction, one of two things usually happens: we either go back to eating sugar, or we start overeating other foods.

Awareness is how we start to break the cycle. We step outside of ourselves and observe ourselves from a distance. We approach ourselves with wonder and curiousity - Isn't that interesting?

If you didn't write your sugar history in phase one, I would suggest doing this exercise. The story of your relationship with your sugar, food and your body can give you clues to foster your awareness. When I wrote my story, I saw several patterns in my own life that helped me understand why I abused sugar.

For example, I noticed that I had used sugar as a way of cheering myself up when I was sad or lonely, from childhood on. I noticed that this was especially true in the cold, winter months.

I saw that I also used sugar to soothe my anxiety. I saw how my constant striving to lose weight caused me to obsess over every bite of food I ate - and how this anxiety fueled my overeating, causing me to eat even more.

Writing my sugar history also helped me see the connection between eating sugar and feeling loved. I come from a large, loud, wonderful extended Italian-Polish family. My favorite childhood memories are the holidays and vacations that I spent with my aunts and uncles and cousins. Sugar was center stage of all those vacations and holidays.

As a young adult separated from my extended family, I craved the sugary treats of my youth. I was trying to recreate those feelings of connection. It really wasn't about the Pepsi or my grandma's apple pie; it was about wanting to feel like that secure, happy, rooted child again.

With this awareness, I started working on my pattern of turning to food - any food - for comfort. While it was a gradual healing process of many years, I've gently learned how to unhook from the desire for food and comfort my real feelings. I don't do this perfectly, but I find I am much more mindful about why - and how - I'm eating. It's a new form of spiritual practice.

In healing my overeating, I learned to foster my creativity. For example, when I was missing my extended family, and a plane ticket was too expensive, I would write letters, look at old family photographs, and call my grandparents on the phone. I'd even wear some of my grandma's jewelry, which she had handed down to me. I sought out creative alternatives to give myself the deep connection that I desired in apple pie.

Sugar may seem like a quick, easy way to solve lots of problems. And, in many ways, it is: it's cheap, socially acceptable, and easy to eat. If you've had an argument with your spouse, it's easier to stuff your frustration in a Snicker's bar than to sit down and have a difficult conversation. It's easier to eat your loneliness via a Ben and Jerry's tub than to take the time and effort to make new friends. It's easier to grab a cookie than to chop vegetables, grill a chicken breast, and make a healthy meal.

But over the long term, those "easy" solutions bring their own problems. The path of sugar abstinence isn't always easy. But it is life changing.

As you continue in your sugar abstinence, you'll need to be equipped to handle life without sugar on a daily basis. In the following tips, I offer advice on how I conquered my own stumbling blocks, tricky situations that tested my resolve. By offering suggestions on coping with unsupportive friends or deprivation, I hope to embolden you so that you realize the universal nature of your experiences. And, most importantly, that these tests can be used to empower your sugar abstinence - and your own inner growth - and not weaken it.

It Really Isn't About The Sugar

Giving up sugar is about a lot more than simply passing on a piece of cake or saying no to a bowl of ice cream. Conquering sugar addiction isn't really about sugar at all. Initially - yes. But once you're free from a chemical dependency on sugar, maintaining abstinence has everything to do with you: how you see yourself, how you treat yourself, how you think about yourself, what you believe, what you fear, and what you feel.

As you navigate a sugar free life, all of those things will come into play. It's as if giving up sugar opens a giant Pandora's box: Are you ready for the consequences? Are you ready to dig deeply into yourself?

Giving up sugar will change your life, and not just because you'll lose weight, stabilize your moods, or eliminate the shame and low self-esteem from bingeing on sugar.

It will change your life because it will put your habits, beliefs, thoughts and feelings under a microscope, and force you to take a good, long look. You'll see your "weaknesses." You'll face the many ways your mind denies or hides from the truth. Giving up sugar will shine a light on all the fears you haven't faced.

It's only by being willing to look in the mirror and face those fears that you'll free yourself from sugar addiction. This is how you stay sugar free. I wish there were an easier way, but I haven't found it.

While self-examination can sometimes feel like a burden, it is, in truth, a gift. This process will help you grow. It will transform your life. It will bring you home to yourself. It will help you question the belief that you're flawed or a mess.

I tell you this not to frighten you, but to embolden you. If this all sounds like too much - *I just want to learn how to say no to the brownies when they call my name, for Pete's sake!* - understand that sugar is not the real enemy. The "enemy" is the belief that we're not okay. Even that isn't an enemy, but a small part of us that needs our love and compassion. It needs to be freed. How do we do this?

Rainer Maria Rilke wrote in *Letters to a Young Poet:* "How should we be able to forget those ancient myths that are at the beginning of all peoples - those myths about dragons that at the last moment turn into princesses. Perhaps all the dragons of our lives are princesses, only waiting to see us, once beautiful and brave. Perhaps everything terrible in our lives is, in its deepest being, something helpless, that wants help from us."

Sugar addiction is a princess disguised as a dragon, not for you to slay, but to love; something helpless that wants your bravery and your courage.

Distinguish Between Physical Cravings And Phantom Cravings

Once you have been sugar free for several weeks, you shouldn't have sugar cravings. In fact, you should be pleasantly surprised by how little you think about sugar at *all*.

If you *are* having sugar cravings, one of three things is usually going on:

1. **You have some other issue going on.** Always look to the simplest explanation first. Could you have low blood sugar? High blood sugar? Another medical problem? Could a prescription medication be the cause? A vitamin deficiency? Out of balance hormones? Seek out medical help to rule out any physical issues first. For example, I've done blood work to uncover a vitamin D deficiency, low blood sugar and locate hormonal imbalances. All were contributing to my eating habits and blah moods.

2. **You've eaten hidden or covert sugars**. You live in the world, so there will be times when you eat sugar unbeknownst to you. You may eat some sugar in a salad dressing in a restaurant, or in a meatloaf at a dinner party. If you notice yourself craving sugar, do a trackback: think back over the last few days and what you ate. Were you eating covert sugars, like overloading on fruit? Were you eating lots of white flour or other processed carbs? Did you go out to eat?

Try and pinpoint the culprit. (This is where a food journal can come in handy.) If you suspect that you ate something that is triggering sugar cravings, be extra vigilant. You may feel off for a few days as your body screams for a sweet hit. Do whatever you have to do to be extra disciplined. Then use this information to help yourself the next time. This is how you discover what foods trigger your sugar sensitivity and which do not, a process of trial and error. Learn from it, and move on.

3. **You're feeling emotionally deprived**. When you're feeling deprived in spirit, this feeling can manifest in the body. Are you craving comfort food, or comfort? Are you wanting the familiar, the routine of eating ice cream? Are you feeling unmoored by all of the changes? I call these phantom cravings, because while they're not biologically based, they feel real.

In my life, I found that I would overeat to compensate for an unmet need or to soothe a blocked feeling. The way out of phantom cravings is nurturing - caring for our needs and feelings.

How can you be kind to yourself? How can you pamper yourself without sugar? Your old habits created a certain pathway, a routine and an expectation. It looked like this: I feel sad=I eat ice cream=I feel better. Granted, the mood lift may be temporary, but the ice cream served you in some way. Create a new pathway that replicates the same feelings that the ice cream generated - a warm feeling of care, empathy, compassion - with a non-sugar substitute.

This means sitting with yourself to uncover the real need underneath the temporary solace of food. Are you worn out and need soothing? Are you agitated? Keyed up? Are you tired and need a boost?

Our needs and feelings are often entertwined. So you may find a need for intimacy (or connection) underneath your feelings of fatigue. Your need for soothing may speak to a greater need for gentleness.

Learning how to care for ourselves without sugar is like good parenting - it takes a lot more time and effort than just saying, "Because I said so." And as with good parenting, the rewards are many.

As you tune into your needs and feelings you create a relationship with yourself. You listen. You take heed. You push less and observe more. Your life flows more than it feels forced.

Granted, none of us are perfect and none of us do this perfectly. All I'm asking is for you to be willing to examine the deeper needs underneath your cravings, to explore the deep, rich territory of your soul. Just listen. Listen, and you will find the voice that knows what to do.

Admit When You're Struggling

Giving up sugar for good means that you will eat differently than most people. Friends and family may think that you're too strict, that you need to relax about food, or that you're attempting the impossible. They may think you're a health food nut.

This can become a sticking point when you're struggling. When you're feeling tempted to eat sugar - for whatever reason - you need to be able to ask for extra support without feeling as if you have to defend your choice to be sugar free in the first place. This takes an odd combination of vulnerability and strength: the strength to stand up for your decision to abstain from sugar, as well as the vulnerability to admit that you're having a difficult time standing by your decision.

The key is to separate the two: asking for extra support doesn't make you a failure, and taking extra measures to help yourself doesn't mean that you aren't serious about being sugar free.

So if the cookies in the house are calling your name, be confident that you can ask your spouse or children to hide them without feeling like you have to defend your sugar abstinence all over again. Better to take the extra care to support yourself and prevent a sugar binge then to remain silent and have to suffer the effects of eating sugar all over again.

Most people like to help. Most people like hearing specific, concrete things they can do to help us - because most of the time, we hide our needs from others. Our directness soothes their anxiety about feeling uncertain about how to help.

Remember Why You Feel So Good

If I can think of one single thing that tripped me the most when I was trying to give up sugar, it was this: I became forgetful. After I had stopped eating sugar for a while, I felt fantastic. My weight, moods, and emotions stabilized; I no longer had sugar cravings. I was free from obsessive thoughts about food.

The problem with this scenario is that I would forget *why* I felt so good. I would be at a party, see the cake, and think, "I'm feeling so good. One piece of chocolate cake won't hurt." It's like I had a temporary case of amnesia: forgetting that the very reason why I felt so good was because I *wasn't* eating sugar.

When you hear the voice of temptation; when you're feeling like a bite of sugar won't hurt you: remember. Remember how that kind of thinking is what kept you locked in sugar addiction in the first place. Remember that you can't have just one piece. Remember that one piece always leads to a desire for more, and more, and more.

The thinking that caused our addiction can not heal it. We get rid of the old to make way for the new. We gave up the old ways of thinking when we gave up sugar. Honor your new truth: that you are choosing to be sugar free, with every choice, with every meal.

Be Disciplined...Without Being Neurotic

I remember watching a cooking show on the Food Network last fall while we were on vacation. Giada de Laurentiis was whipping up hot chocolate, a batch of waffles; homemade pasta and gelato. I loved the joy she expressed for food: both in the preparation and eating of it.

That image has stayed with me. There are times when I wish I was like Giada, to be one of those women who can eat whatever they want and stay trim and healthy. I wish I could eat like the French do - a little bit of everything, including dessert.

But that is not my biochemistry. And yet this doesn't mean that I can't be joyful about food. The essence of what Giada represents to me - freedom from thinking about food in terms of fat grams, carb counts, sugar vs. no sugar, or calories - can be found in a sugar free diet.

I, too, can enjoy a wide variety of foods, even while I abstain from many others. I, too, can relish in setting a beautiful table and cooking a fabulous meal.

A sugar free life doesn't have to be neurotic. I can relax about food even as I carefully approach it.

Cooking without sugar means I often have to use my creativity. But there are still so many wonderful, tasty foods that I can eat. I can embrace food - after all, it's a gift to be cherished and enjoyed - even while I'm disciplined about what foods I eat. You can, too.

Know What Sugar Abstinence Can and Can't Do

Giving up sugar will change your life. No doubt about it. It can give you back your life, if you were harangued by food cravings, depression, vacillating moods, overeating, low self esteem and obesity.

But eliminating sugar won't solve all your problems. It may not even cure all your problems. If you use food for comfort giving up sugar may not be enough. You may find yourself overeating nuts and chicken breasts. If you have low self esteem, you may find that it's a problem beyond the shame you felt about abusing sugar.

This can be devastating. If you thought that giving up sugar was it, the thing to heal you, what happens when it doesn't bring you the happiness you sought? What happens if giving up sugar doesn't fix your problems? What if you still feel depressed from time to time? What if you still overeat?

We all have our stumbling blocks. Giving up sugar won't change this. Have you ever heard Jon Kabat-Zinn's phrase, "Wherever you go, there you are?" That's how it is after sugar. You're still you - just the you without the sugar addiction.

While sugar abstinence can cure some things, it can't cure the human condition. We all have challenges. We all peel the onion: revisiting our issues over and over again, but at a deeper and deeper level. We all experience times of grief, sorrow, and frustration. This is part of the gig of being alive.

I often look at myself as if I were a home remodeling project. I'll be at peace when I have it "all together" - when the remodeling is complete. But, just like a house, there's always something. The beautiful refinished floors get scratched and need repolished; the paint chips and requires touch ups; the new kitchen eventually becomes dated.

Life is like that, too. In my head, I have this imaginary time when I've got it all together, when my life is seamless, when I've healed all my issues. It's this same thinking that leads me forward, ignoring the present moment, imagining some future time when life is perfect, or better: when I'm down to my ideal weight; when I'm exercising more regularly, when I'm debt free.

But there will always be something. Impermanence, evolution, change are inherent parts of life itself. It's what makes life, alive. That moment when we've got it all together, when we're no longer being pulled or prodded or tumbled around? That's called death.

So while sugar abstinence can heal many things, it's greater power lies in the release of your moral courage, the intention that you sent out into the world when you resolved to release sugar's hold on your life. Every day that you face sugar and remain steadfast, your confidence grows. Every day that you take responsibility for your health and happiness, you feed your evolution. Every day that you choose chard over chocolate you prove that you are a capable human being, freely choosing the arduous road of growth.

Make peace with the impermanence of life, of accepting that there will always be something. This brings me to one of my favorite quotes, an anonymous saying I once saw on a coffee cup: "Peace. It does not mean to be in a place where there is no noise, trouble, or hard work. It means to be in the midst of those things and still be calm in your heart."

Fear and food

One of the reasons I abused food for years was that I was afraid. I was afraid of my own potential. As long as I was regularly feeling sick and bloated from overeating, as long as I was drowning in shame and depression, I had every excuse to shut myself away from the world. How could I pursue my dreams? I was just trying to make it through another day.

It sounds odd that we can be frightened of our own success. But this is often the case with self destructive behaviors. We are terrified of putting ourselves out there, of daring to push beyond our comfort zones. After all, we might fail. We might not measure up. We can avoid the heartbreak of failure by not trying, by staying in our warm cocoon of familiarity.

What if giving up sugar does heal your issues and frees you to pursue your passions? But instead of feeling delighted, what if you feel, oddly, deflated? What happens when you get what you want, but it doesn't make you happy?

If you blamed sugar for your lack of success, for your unhappiness, for your frailty, when you remove sugar, guess what? You remove the blame. All of a sudden, your happiness lands smack dab in your lap. It rests on your shoulders.

What would your life look like if you weren't afraid to give up sugar? If you had the courage to push out of your comfort zones?

Be prepared for these questions. Be prepared for the vacuum you create when you remove sugar from your life. Do you know what fills this empty void, now that sugar no longer runs the show? God. Your deepest passions, longings; hopes and dreams. The still small voice that you buried under mounds of ice cream and chocolate chip cookies.

The Discomfort Of Change Will Pass

In the beginning, life without sugar will feel strange. You'll go to the movies and feel weird without munching on candy. Christmas will feel lackluster without a marathon baking session. A birthday without cake? Dinner without dessert?

These experiences may feel as if something is missing. Like something's off. Like the holidays or dinners aren't complete.

You'll long for sugar, not due to any physical cravings, but to feel the comforting pull of familiarity. This is normal, and true with any major change. My friend Jeannie, who inspired me to give up sugar, says that change is difficult because it's like putting our pants on backwards. For a time, it feels wrong; inside out.

For a time, giving up sugar may feel all wrong. Not eating dessert will feel uncomfortable. You may feel unmoored by all of the changes. You may wonder why you gave up sugar in the first place.

These feelings are common to any major change. But over time, not eating sugar will become your new normal. You'll be in the routine of not eating sugar, and those experiences will feel "right." You'll have new memories of going to the movies, Christmas time, or dinners without sugar - memories that will build upon one another and reciprocate your success.

If you're feeling inside out, unmoored, and strange: trust that these feelings will pass. Everything shifts, even discomfort.

What About Backlash? Criticism?

What may surprise you about giving up sugar - or making any positive change in your life - is the seeming lack of support from other people in your life. When you understand why this happens, it becomes easier not to take other people's criticism personally.

We are all mirrors for each other. When you ate sugar, you were a mirror; when you stopped eating sugar, you are also a mirror. If you're reflecting back to others something they don't want to see in themselves - such as their own sugar addiction, weight problem, or other health issue - they may lash out at you. They'll project their feelings onto you. So instead of facing their own problems, they criticize you. It's a natural human reaction, and we all do it.

So if your spouse, sister, mother, or friends are criticizing your sugar free life, try and look at the situation from their perspective. Maybe they're feeling envious of your success. (We've all done that, too.) Maybe they're feeling threatened by the change of the status quo. Maybe they're intimidated, because your ability to make changes in your life makes them aware of the changes they'd like to make in their own. Maybe they're uncomfortable, because you've become an uncomfortable mirror, highlighting the places in their own life where they need to change.

The key is to understand that, no matter the reasons for their behavior, their criticism is about *them*, not you. Forgive them, and let it go. Don't take it personally. I once read, "What other people think of me is none of my business."

What other people think of you is none of your business.

Your business is supporting yourself in the best way that you know how. This includes finding ways to have a joyful, sugar free life. Hopefully, over time, as your joy, ease, and confidence grows, this will serve as a beacon, a light for your friends and family. Hopefully, over time, they will feel inspired by your example, without a need to dim it. In the meantime, keep your focus on where you're going, on what you want, not on the stumbling blocks - including unsupportive loved ones - in the way.

More Thoughts On Facing Criticism

It would be wonderful if we could support one another, 100% of the time. But this is wishful thinking. We're all human. We all have moments when we're less than kind, less than gracious, less than supportive.

People may criticize your choices. They may try to get you to eat sugar. They may try to persuade you that one bite won't hurt. They may think that your sugar addiction is all in your head.

Relax. It's not personal. I know it feels personal. I know when someone calls you a health nut or neurotic or overcontrolling (or the many other adjectives I've heard to describe my eating habits), that it hurts.

But it's really about the other person, and not you. When people make snarky comments, they are expressing *their* beliefs, perceptions, and judgments. You don't have to make them your own. They are your beliefs or perceptions only if you believe them. That is what leads to feelings of anger, defensiveness, and insult. If you're at peace with yourself, their comments won't hook you.

At the same time, have compassion: have you ever been critical or snarky towards someone else? When we recognize that we all harbor a critical side, that we all have moments of pettiness, we can relax when we face this side in others.

Recognize that you don't know the whole story. Have you ever miscommunicated? Said something that was misinterpreted? Failed to communicate your true meaning? We all have.

Likewise, we all have been the recipient of such failed communication. We often proscribe judgments to other people's words when we are unaware of their true intention. We create a story - "She doesn't accept me because she's criticizing my sugar abstinence," construing comments as insults, assuming that the other person meant to insult us. But we just don't know. And often, they aren't insulting us at all: just communicating in an insensitive manner.

Reframe it. When you are being criticized by others, how can you frame this event so that it supports your growth? Even when you are being treated unkindly, you still have a choice with what you do with that pain.

You can frame hurtful comments in two ways: "Other people don't like me. People don't accept me as who I am. I'm not good enough as I am. I'm always being picked on." Or, "I'm so glad I love and accept myself, even with my sugar abstinence. I'm being given an opportunity to love myself unconditionally. What an opportunity for me to practice self-care."

Yes, I know that it's much easier to feel wronged when you've been hurt. I know it feels better, too - in the short term. But it's your life, your time, and your energy that you're expending. Those hours you spent, getting angry and sad and feeling hurt by someone's rude comment? Those were hours you can never reclaim. Those hours were your very life.

We forgive others, not for their sake, but for our own.

Failure Can Be A Good Thing

What happens when you've been sugar free for days, weeks, or months, and you slip up and have a piece of chocolate cake?

You may call it a failure. I think failure is a good thing.

Yes, you read that sentence correctly. A *good* thing.

Failure is how we learn. It's how we fine tune our sugar abstinence. It's how we find our trigger points, those areas that still need our attention.

Failure is what paves the way for our success. So, if you dug into the brownie pan, look at this as a learning opportunity: What were you thinking when you gave into the sugar? Did you try to reason with yourself, that you could just eat one brownie and go back to your sugar abstinence the next day?

Don't question the sugar. Question what preceded the sugar. Usually, when I gave into sugar, it was because I was persuading myself that I could eat one bite of sugar and be okay. It's almost as if I forget how addictive sugar is when I haven't eaten it in a while. But here's the genius of a slip-up: it will remind you very quickly why you *don't* eat sugar. The pull to overeat, the mood swings, the depression: all of those consequences very quickly remind you: "Yes. This is why I stopped eating sugar."

So look at this situation as a reminder of why you gave up sugar in the first place. So, yes, it may take time for you to get back on track. Yes, this may mean enduring the discomfort of detoxing off sugar. Yes, it may mean being extra vigilant for a week. You can do all these things as you also take this experience and learn from it.

There will be another time when you'll feel sugar's call. I guarantee it. This time you'll be prepared. This time you'll remember - *Oh yeah. There's that nutty voice again, trying to convince me that one bite won't hurt.* You'll remember and you'll know what to do.

Everything exists to help us grow and learn.

Let Your Friends and Family Be

When we achieve a goal, such as giving up sugar, it's natural that we want to share our success with others. It's also natural that we may notice others around us who may benefit from our sugar abstinence. But I would caution you to be careful, because sharing can easily turn to judgment and one-upmanship.

Nobody likes a show-off. Nobody likes the food police. If you approach your friends and family with a holier-than-thou attitude about their diet, with you as their diet savior, expect a backlash.

Yes, you may recognize your family as sugar addicted. After all, sugar addiction tends to be hereditary. Yes, you may be able to help your friends lose weight. But this is not the time and the place to herald change.

People can only change when they're ready. When they're not ready, they won't be able to hear the message. They'll resist it. Another way of saying this is: Don't offer loved ones food or diet or weight loss advice unless it's asked for. Period.

We all want to be loved and accepted. While we are all usually very aware of our sticking points - those areas of our lives that cause us pain - we don't want them flung in our face. We want to feel as if our friends and family love us unconditionally; that while, they may encourage us to grow and change, it's not a prerequisite for their love. You want this. Your friends and family want this.

So, while you give yourself love and compassion, give it to others. If you see a loved one struggling with their own sugar addiction, say a prayer for them. But don't sneak in comments, slyly offer your opinion, or take away their plate.

When you offer your loved ones the freedom to make their own choices, and to live their own lives - even if you don't agree with them, your grace often comes back to you, as you receive the same respect from others.

And, then, you may be delightfully surprised. As you stay focused on your health, and your abstinence, other people will take notice. They will see the positive changes, and curious, they may decide to take a closer look. When they start asking questions, that is the time to cast your pearls of wisdom. Illuminate the path, and show the way. Now that the student has appeared, the teacher, too, is ready.

Look At Meeting Your Various Needs Without Sugar

Marshall Rosenberg is a psychologist who created non-violent communication to help create gentler relationships. He obesrved that our needs drive our behavior. These needs can include connection, love, order, beauty, joy, self-expression, safety, security, or creativity. When you think about sugar's appeal, it's easy to limit it's popularity to taste. Well, it tastes good so it meets a need for pleasure. But what else does sugar do? What needs does sugar meet (or has met) in your life?

Sugar has given me comfort, security, a sense of order, routine and familiarity. It has given me pleasure, and joy, a way of connecting with others. It has fed my self-esteem, such as when I make a fabulous cake or other dessert for my family. It has been an outlet for my creativity, when I use it in baking. It has assuaged my loneliness, such as when I make the pineapple cookies I used to make with my deceased grandmother. When I get together with my girlfriends to exchange cookies at Christmastime, sugar meets my need for connection and community. Sugar allows me to give to others, when I offer friends and neighbors baked goodies. Sugar meets my need for fun - I think about candy at the movies; ice cream on the beach.

When you subtract sugar from these equations, it can feel like a gaping hole is left in its place. The trick is to reframe your thinking: how can you meet these needs without sugar? This is where creative alternatives come into play. This is where you have to consciously separate the love from the sugar. Keep the love; omit the sugar.

Here are a few concrete examples of how this might manifest in your life: Instead of trading cookies with your girlfriends, can you host a spa exchange, where you trade homemade bath salts and body oils? If cooking is one way that you show love for your family, can you channel that energy into cooking healthy foods that both you and they can enjoy, such as a fantastic soup, customized omelets, interesting salads, or a beautiful roast? Can you wear a piece of your grandmother's jewelry, or hang her picture in your home, or play a card game with your children that you used to play with her instead of connecting with her through baking?

There are many ways to meet our needs. We tend to narrowly focus on meeting our needs instead of expanding the container. Then when that option is no longer available, we feel stuck.

How can we be more playful? More open to new ideas? Experiment. Brainstorm. Let yourself think of all sorts of wild ideas. Let your inner child out to play.

Figure Out What Matters Most To You

Okay: find ways to honor your needs. But what if you have opposing needs? What if you have a need for beauty, and you desire a slim, fit body so that you can wear beautiful clothes? But what if you also have a need for comfort; to eat foods - like sugar - that give you pleasure. Here's the tricky part: Eating those foods doesn't give you the slim body that you're desiring. What do you do? Which need do you honor over the other?

First, I would question this all or nothing thinking that says that you can't meet both needs. I believe you can have both, and achieve the essence of what you want, but perhaps not in the form that you want.

Here's what I mean: I like to feel nurtured and pampered. For years, I met this need by eating sugar. Now that I don't eat sugar, I still have a need for nurturing and pampering. So I made a list. I made a list of non-sugar alternatives that make me feel loved and supported. This list includes spending an afternoon by myself in a bookstore; food treats like macadamia nut butter or almond butter; going out dancing or out to hear live music; reading poetry in bed on a rainy afternoon; filling my home with scented candles; buying myself fresh flowers; a hot cup of tea and a good book; taking a nap. These things give me comfort - the feeling of being nurtured, the ability to rest when I'm tired, help for when I'm overwhelmed - the *essence* of what I want, without the heavy emotional price tag from eating sugar.

Too many times we fill our lives with inferior substitutes, cheap comforts that stand in the way of what we really want. We buy something because it's on sale, instead of saving our money and waiting to purchase what we really want. We eat junk food, mindlessly surf the internet, buy cheap merchandise we don't need, and read gossip magazines for the quick hit, the cheap thrill they give us. But all of these things are the spiritual equivalent of empty calories: they may give us an initial surge of energy, but after the crash, we're feeling even emptier inside.

Yes, it takes more time and effort to chop vegetables and make a beautiful salad than it does to grab a candy bar when you're hungry. Yes, saving for the cashmere sweater that makes your heart sing may mean waiting several months to buy it, versus the immediate gratification for the acrylic sweater that's $19.99. Reading a book may take more energy than reading celebrity gossip, but gossip leaves a bad taste in your mouth.

Slow down. Lower your expectations. Accept that eating healthy foods, taking excellent care of yourself, and staying away from sugar may take more of your time. But think of the payoff: think of all of those hours you spent bemoaning your excess weight, or bingeing on sugar, or hiding in your house because you were ashamed of your weight or your bingeing.

Think of freeing that time to serve your self care.

Honor Your Many Selves

While we each have many different needs, we also have different selves. When I speak of our selves, I'm not thinking of our roles - parent, co-worker, friend. I'm talking about the different aspects of our personalities: Our interests, hobbies, desires, and passions.

You may feel like there are many yous: maybe you have a fashionista who loves beautiful clothes, putting on a dress and heels, getting made-up and playing all versions of adult dress-up. Maybe you have a foodie who loves cooking for others and who relishes all kinds of food. Maybe a part of you is a health nut who is into nutrition, health and the environment. Maybe you have an inner jock who is super fit and competitive.

These are just a few ideas. Who are your selves? What are the different aspects of your personality?

Now think about those personalities in relation to sugar. How have those personalities affected your eating habits? Does your inner foodie tempt you into baking fabulous, creative desserts? Does your fashionista scold you for eating sugar, because it leads to weight gain, limiting your choice of clothes from your closet? Does your earth mother try and persuade you to eat a vegetarian diet, to reduce your impact on the world by eating less meat?

Forgive me if this sounds a bit woo-woo, but it's important to acknowledge these various selves as you go about your sugar abstinence. No, this doesn't mean that you have multiple personality disorder. This just means that, like the rest of the human beings who live on this planet, you are comprised of many, often conflicting likes and dislikes. None of us is one dimensional.

Imagine that you're meeting your various selves for tea. Talk to them. What are their fears? What frightens them about your sugar abstinence? What needs do they have?

After you've given your various selves a chance to speak, brainstorm. Think about ways you can meet their needs, and minimize their fears so that your various selves will support your decision to abstain from sugar, rather than sabotage it.

Invite your selves to help you. Tell your foodie: Can you help me think of some chicken recipes that are flavorful and exciting? Reassure your inner athlete: you can still run even if you don't carbo-load.

You may feel like your different selves are bickering siblings, all trying to compete for your attention, love, and time. They all want to be counted. They all want an outlet. When they don't have one, they get a bit cranky, like a child that throws a tantrum to get noticed. You can fix this by operating from an approach of unconditional love and acceptance - where all aspects of yourself are allowed to express themselves. There's enough room in your life for all your selves...even without sugar.

Reduce stressors

Finding ways to reduce your stress will not only help you resist sugar in times of anxiety, it will also help you from overreacting in other ways. A great way to lower the stress in your life is by adding margin.

What is margin? Margin is the wiggle room you leave around the edges; a cushion; what keeps an inconvenience from morphing into a calamity. It's insurance; a back-up plan; a safety net.

A marginless life amounts to living on the edge. Doing things just in time. Living paycheck to paycheck. Waiting until the last minute. Stuffing too much into a day. Not taking into account the unexpected emergencies or situations that inevitably arise.

A margin-less life creates stress and chaos. It leaves you vulnerable to sugar cravings. You can live margin-less and be fine...as long as everything goes according to plan. But when the unexpected occurs, you don't have any space in which to fall. You move from barely hanging on, to free falling.

Margin comes in many forms: an emergency fund for unexpected bills or financial difficulties; a pantry or freezer that's stocked with quick meals for busy nights; a support circle - friends, family and neighbors that will help you in a pinch, whether it be picking up a child from school, lending you a hand when your car is in the shop, or counseling you through a difficult time.

Margin can be a relaxed schedule, where you leave time between appointments to eat lunch, or to simply transition from one activity to the next. Margin can be a relaxed mindset, where you accept the change of plans when a baby is teething and fussy or a child is home with the flu.

Living with margin makes life more joyful. Less anxious. Less dramatic. While we always have a choice in how we react to life's snafus, it's much easier to stay off the sugar when we're not living so close to the bone.

Ways To Add Margin In Your Life

Plan time in your schedule for regular meals. Eating on the go, or skipping meals often leads to poor food choices; you give into sugar because you're hungry or because it's most convenient.

Get up earlier to allow for a more relaxed morning routine or morning exercise. This starts you day with a positive intention: the signal that you are putting your needs, first. When I feel bulldozed by other people's needs and put myself last, I substitute food for the care that I'm not giving myself. You should know by now that this is not usually in the form of broccoli or celery sticks.

Stock your home with healthy foods that you can eat. I have "fake it" meals in my freezer for those times when I haven't gone to the store and I'm out of fresh, sugar free foods. This includes salmon burgers, frozen vegetables, and other quick cooking fish. That way, I know I can cook something healthy for myself without resorting to pasta - a no no for me with the wheat flour.

You're Not A Victim

It's easy to think of yourself as weak or a victim if you're sugar sensitive. You might feel sorry for yourself: Why can't I eat so many yummy foods like a normal person? You might feel like you're damaged goods: Why do I have to be so careful about food? I'm so screwed up - I can't even eat a few apples without whacking out my body!

I've experienced both sets of feelings: feelings of weakness, as well as feelings of victimhood. My husband said something to me once that has stuck with me ever since. I was in tears, telling him how ashamed I felt for being so fragile. "I can't even tolerate food like a normal person!" I cried. "I feel like the world is too much for me - I don't fit in here! I'm such a weakling, I'm pathetic."

This was my husband's reply; what I offer to you for those times when you feel weak, pathetic, fragile, high maintenance, too sensitive, and like you don't belong: "Karly, you're not weak; you're strong. You're the most disciplined person I've ever met. Your food choices and the habits you put into place to take care of your body show your strength, your willingness to put aside your desires for a higher goal. That's not fragility; that's courage. That's boldness. It's inspiring, what you do."

You are not a victim. You are not weak. You are not fragile. You are disciplined. You are selective. And this discipline proves your strength, on a daily, hourly basis. Be proud of what you're doing, the choices you're making, the ways you care for yourself.

Sometimes You'll Get Sick Of Thinking About Sugar

When we first embark on a major change like giving up sugar, we are gung-ho, hard charging, motivated, and excited. We are like a group of Marines, armed and ready for battle. This is especially true if you gained significant benefits: if the excess pounds are falling off, if your mood is improved, if your sex life is better. After your sugar detox, you may feel like you're on top of the world: like you are, for the first time, free. This is understandable. You've removed a huge block from your life: of *course* you're excited.

But while the sugar success is real, and a huge weight has been lifted off your chest, your enthusiasm will wane. You will go through many phases in your sugar healing. Sometimes you'll be gung ho and passionate about your sugar free life. At other times, you may feel sad about not eating sugar. Another time, you may be sick of sugar, or sick of *thinking* about food and sugar at all. This is normal, too.

During those times when you're sick of thinking about sugar, honor that need. Give yourself a break. Don't make sugar abstinence your life; it's purpose is to free yourself to live your life, not to *become* it.

Don't be like a teenage girl whose whole life revolves around her new boyfriend, thinking that as long as she has him, she doesn't need anything or anyone else. Yes, you need to abstain from sugar. But you still need your friends. You still need your family. You still need your faith. You still need to exercise and make choices that make your body feel good. You still need your hobbies and passions and interests outside of food.

If you're sick of reading about sugar - and that includes this book - put it down. Pick up a novel. Play a game of basketball with your kids. Teach yourself a new skill. Paint your bathroom. Fill your life with things that honor your passions, your needs, and your values, so that your sugar abstinence serves your life, and not the other way around.

Embrace Discipline As A Kindness

I know that sugar free living can feel like a lot of rules, don'ts, and restrictions. It's easy - and natural - to resist the very things that will most help us. No one likes being told what to do...and this includes ourselves telling us what to do. It's important to approach your food choices as a way of nurturing yourself, not as a way of punishing yourself.

Unless you frame your sugar abstinence in a positive manner, it will be impossible to stick with your eating habits over the long haul. You have to accept that eating sugar free isn't a temporary solution or a diet, but a way of life.

It's easy to initially be excited about a big change. We're all gung ho in the beginning. But as the changes start to sink in, and you've gone many days without a sweet hit, it's easy to start to feel resistant, deprived, and like sugar free living is no fun at all.

When I start to feel this way, I remind myself of how crazy sugar made me feel…and how great I feel when I don't eat it. I remind myself that I'm choosing to stay away from sugar not because of a few pounds, but because of my very life.

I also turn toward my feelings. I don't run from the deprivation, I lean into it. I may even have a conversation with it. I ask myself, "What am I feeling?"

Often what I find under deprivation is fear. I may be afraid that I'll never have pleasure again. I may feel frightened that I won't get the soothing and comforting I need.

I'm anticipating and fearing future pain.

Once I get in touch with my feelings, then I offer them care. I put my hand on my heart and I tell myself, "I care about your suffering." I cry my tears. I label my feelings as, "Fear." Or, "Grief." I keep labeling the tumult of feelings and caring for them.

When my feelings are cared for, I can move to action. I can say, "What do I need?" I may not need to do anything. Often, caring for my feelings softens them enough that I don't have to give myself any further soothing.

If I need more support, than I can decide how I want to respond. Do I want to reach out to others? Do I want to offer myself some non-sugar comfort? By soothing my feelings, I've created the space to pause and respond differently than my habitual patterns.

Be A Diet Detective

The key about maintaining a sugar abstinence over time is paying attention. While you may stay clear of overt sugars - things like chocolate cake and candy bars - you may get tripped over the sneaky, sly sugars: things like ketchup, fruit juice, or potato chips. How deep you want to take your sugar abstinence is up to you, whether you limit all forms of sugar, or just foods with added sugars.

Regardless of how loose or structured your eating is, a successful sugar abstinence entails a willingness to experiment, coupled with mindful observation. If you want to know if ketchup triggers your sugar cravings, eat some, and observe what happens. If you find yourself drooling over a candy bar the next day, you'll know that ketchup is a food you might want to stay away from.

I'm not your diet police. No one is. How you carry out your sugar abstinence is up to you. How you define sugar abstinence is up to you. While I can offer how I define sugar abstinence in my own life, I am me, and you are you. You will have to fine tune the particulars on your own, over time.

I know this feels scary. I know it would be easier to have a list of good foods and bad foods. But you need to be the leader of your own life. You need to take ownership and responsibility for your sugar abstinence.

You are the one who lives with it and who reaps the benefits. So pay attention. If you start experiencing sugar cravings, stop, pause and observe what's going on around you. If you discover other foods that trigger you, do your best to abstain from them. We're not after perfection, but we do maintain a proactive approach: a practice of mindful observation.

Ingrain New Habits Into Your Life

If you spent a significant part of your day thinking about sugar and other carbs, or eating sugar and other carbs, you'll need to fill that time with other activities. This is particularly true if you binged on sugar in the afternoon or at night. Your fingers will itch to eat. Your old familiar patterns - as destructive as they may be - may call to you with their familiarity.

Counter these feelings with new patterns. Start an evening ritual of an after-dinner bath or shower. If being in the kitchen is too tempting after dinnertime, ask your family if they'd be willing to clean up the kitchen.

Another handy trick is to brush your teeth right after dinner - an action that signals your body that mealtime is over.

New patterns, habits, alternatives: these all become ingrained over time. As you replace old destructive habits with new, positive ones, they'll become automatic, a positive, self perpetuating cycle.

See Yourself As Resilient

How do you feel when you encounter a setback? How do you feel when your goals don't come easily, but require daily effort, or months or years of work?

Life often feels like two steps forward, one step back. When we're stepping back, we can feel lost. We can lose our momentum. Our confidence. We may trap ourselves with negative thinking, believing the inevitable challenges means that we can't or won't succeed. We doubt ourselves: our ability, our courage, our determination.

Our doubts may even cause us to question our desire for something in the first place. You may long for the days before you knew about how bad sugar was for you.

Yes, ignorance is bliss. In many ways, life *was easier* when you weren't holding yourself to such a high level of accountability. But while you weren't enduring the sacrifices, neither were you enjoying the rewards.

If you're facing a setback, I say to you: you are resilient. You are capable. You can meet the challenges that come your way. Think back to all of those inspirational, rags-to-riches stories; the overnight success stories, the underdog sports stories, where the once laughable team comes from behind to claim their victory. Think of every person you know who has achieved their dreams, and think of the courage and strength they employed on a daily basis to get there.

Challenges aren't meant to discourage us; to tempt us; to bring us to failure. We're challenged because tests are the very thing we need to grow. Just as our muscles grow from use - we make them stronger by increasing the amount of weight we lift, or the number of miles we run - we make our internal muscles stronger by increasing the forces we apply to them.

So keep showing up. If you're going to the gym every day, determined to finally lose your excess weight, and the scale isn't budging, keep showing up.

If you're trying to kick your sugar habit, and you're facing continual temptation, wondering if you'll ever feel free, keep showing up.

If you're trying to love your body, and you still look at your body in disgust, keep showing up.

You are resilient. When you fall down, you pick yourself up. When you mess up, you dust yourself off, and start over. When you feel discouraged, like you'll never change, believe that you are changing, one challenge at a time.

Don't Make Problems Of Your Problems

My friend has a saying: "I refuse to make problems of my problems." He told me this while relaying the story of how, with his car packed for a cross country move from California to North Carolina, his car was broken into, resulting in the loss of his most valuable possessions. (The less important things were in the moving van.) His clothes were even stolen. Yet he smiled while telling me this story; confident that it would all work out.

We all have problems: things break, accidents happen, children act up, spouses argue, families disagree. But we don't have to compound our problems in our heads with worry, anxiety, fear or stress. If, in the midst of difficulty, we can pause, and silence our monkey mind (the endless chatter that goes into overdrive whenever something goes wrong,) we often discover that solutions present themselves.

So let's say you're flying to visit your family, and the beautiful, sugar free lunch you've packed for the day of traveling is confiscated at the airport. You start to panic: what am I going to eat all day? If I get too hungry, I'll be temped to eat sugar. There's never any healthy food at airports!

This inner commentary, insistent and disaster driven, is making problems of your problems. It's imagining worse case scenarios. But that doesn't mean it's true.

Instead, quiet your commentary, and give yourself space and quiet. In the quiet, you often find solutions to your problems: Oh, I can call my mom and dad and have them bring food to the airport for me, so I have something to eat as soon as I get off the plane. Airports are making an effort to have healthier food. I bet I can find a grilled chicken breast somewhere to eat. Oh, and I've seen nuts and apples at many airports, too. I think I can assemble something that will tide me over for the day.

The thing is, even the biggest mess, eventually, gets cleaned up. Even the largest problem gets solved. If we open our minds to solutions, instead of magnifying our problems in our minds, we find that everything, eventually, works out.

When You Mess Up, Reach Out

When we screw up, our natural, human reaction is to hide. If we slip up and eat sugar, instead of reaching out to others, we usually avoid our friends, loved ones, and family.

As uncomfortable as it may make you feel to admit your screw ups to others, it is absolutely essential to a successful sugar abstinence. When we avoid our loved ones, we avoid the very people who can help us get back on track. It's important when we mess up to get out of our heads: to stop the endless ruminating that is often worse than the offense itself. Our inner critic is relentless. Reaching out to others quiets its nitpicking.

Often, we don't share our slip ups because we're afraid of being judged, of being vulnerable and looking less than perfect. But, in my experience, other people are much more gracious towards our mistakes than we are. We are our own harshest critics.

When we're berating ourselves for slipping up and eating sugar, we often feel beside ourselves. Have you ever thought about that phrase? We use it as a way of describing someone who's full of remorse or regret.

But look closer, at its literal meaning: It means you aren't whole. You're separated from yourself. You're in a space of disconnect. When you're beside yourself, it's almost as if you have a split personality: like there is one part of you that is feeling terrible, and another part that is *judging* you for feeling terrible. This is a pretty accurate description of what's happening.

So how do you integrate both parts of yourself, and find peace? How do you move on?

1. **Offer yourself comfort**. When you're feeling remorseful, you don't need to berate yourself any further. You already feel badly. What you need is comfort, compassion and kindness so that you can objectively look at what happened and find ways to act differently the next time.

I comfort myself just as I would comfort a small child: I cuddle in bed with a pillow or stuffed animal and cry, and I talk to myself in reassuring tones, "It's okay, honey. You're going to be all right." I also picture someone from my childhood who gave me unconditional love- usually a family member or friend - and visualize that person comforting me in the present moment. All of these things help ease the sting.

2. **Get your story out of your head**. My tendency, when I'm hurting, is to distance myself from friends and loved ones. I feel ashamed for messing up, so I try and hide it as much as possible. However, when I break through this barrier, and share my pain with a compassionate listener, I find immediate relief. It's easy to delve into overthinking and excessive rumination, where

you get trapped in a mental rut, going over and over something in your mind. Telling your story - whether on paper, in a journal, or spoken aloud, to a friend - stops the spin cycle and enables you to find the exit ramp.

3. **Give yourself self acceptance**. It's easy to offer yourself approval when you're on your "best" behavior. But what about when you mess up? What about when you're less than perfect? Do you offer yourself love and support at those times, as well?

It's ironic that these low times are when you need self-approval the most. Without self-approval, you increase the split between your personality and your spirit, so your deepest source of aid remains unavailable. It's operating at half throttle; you can't access your spirit, so that you can move from remorse to acceptance. Self-acceptance reconnects this broken link. It opens your thinking, so that you can see why you slipped up and ate the sugar in the first place, and how you can meet your needs in a healthier way the next time.

Ask Others For Help

For years, I was afraid to ask others for help. Often, my fear stemmed from a desire to appear strong and independent. Feeling needy made me feel vulnerable, as if someone would criticize me for not being more "together."

In her book *There Are No Mistakes*, Eleanor Wiley writes about the importance of vulnerability. She says one of the dangers of acting as if we have it all together is that we disallow others to help us when we're hurting.

For much of my life, it was very difficult for me to ask for help when I needed it. What if someone says no? What if I ask for something inappropriate and I look like a social misfit? What if I look, well, needy?

I had this sense that something was wrong with me, that I had all of these huge, insatiable needs that could never be filled. If I asked for help in meeting them, others would reject me for the very neediness I sought to remedy. I felt that I, and my needs, were just too much.

This, my friends, is another version of the lie that I am not okay, just as I am; that there is something about me that is inherently flawed or unacceptable. The key is this is a lie.

The truth is, we need each other. You need other people in order to live a sugar free life. Other people need you to live their best life. Ask for help. Ask others to come to your aid. Believe that you are worthy of care and support.

If someone can't help you, recognize that it's not personal. If one person says no, keep asking until you find a yes.

As you ask, give to others. No, this doesn't mean running around, making yourself crazy putting everyone else's needs above your own. But when you can help out, help out. And accept that when others can help you, they will.

Find The Good In Your Sugar Sensitivity

Here's an exercise for you: take a paper and pen, and write down everything you dislike about your sugar sensitivity. Be brutally honest. Don't censor yourself. Be petty, vain, and egotistical. Now think of three things that are good about your sugar sensitivity.

Here's what I wrote down when I did this: I hate that I can't eat sweets. I wish I could eat candy at the movies. I don't like being so fragile, having to be so disciplined about the food I eat lest it negatively effect my mental health.

Here are my three good things: My sugar sensitivity makes me more compassionate towards other people and their addictions. My sugar sensitivity forces me to take extra good care of myself. Because of my sugar sensitivity, I eat a really, really healthy diet, which gives me energy and good health. Being a sugar addict has helped me grow and take responsibility for my life.

This exercise left me trembling with awe: I felt as if the light bulbs all clicked on in my head at once, in a giant, "A-ha" moment. Finding the good in things I really, really disliked about my sugar sensitivity opened my awareness, so I could see the gift in "the bad." It silenced my need to judge my sugar sensitivity as "good" or "bad" in the first place.

Even when my body (or my life) unfolds in ways I don't like, I'm still okay. I'm still more than okay, actually: who's to say that I'm not better off for being sugar sensitive? Who's to say that you're not better off for being sugar sensitive?

Dealing With Loved Ones Who Cook

A friend was telling me about how she's been wanting to eat differently and lose weight for several months now, but has been frustrated in her efforts by her husband. Her husband loves to cook rich food and make homemade bread: the very things that she's trying not to eat. When she politely refuses to eat his meals, his feelings are hurt. And this is from a couple who've been happily married for over 35 years! My friend sighed in frustration: "I just eat the food, because I don't want to hurt his feelings."

I share this story with you to show the many ways that food gets complicated in the context of a relationship. Of course we don't want to inflict any unnecessary suffering on our loved ones. And yet, as long as we put others' needs above our own, we'll continue to eat food we don't really want to eat.

It's important, when you're confronted with a similar situation, to separate someone's love from the food. We all have people in our lives who are kind, giving and who love to shower us with fabulous cooking. It's one of the primary ways we show care.

And yet we can separate the love and kindness from the food itself. If we gently explain why we don't eat certain foods, we may hurt someone's feelings. And yet their feelings about our dietary choices are their business. We can be compassionate towards their feelings as we are also kind. And as we also stand our ground.

If your loved ones typically show their love by cooking you sugary foods, their feelings will probably be hurt when you refuse to eat their love offerings. One way to deal with this situation is to be proactive: to let loved ones know before the huge Sunday dinner that you won't be eating any sugar.

Another suggestion is to find a creative alternative: if your spouse likes to cook for you, channel that energy into cooking foods that you can eat. Maybe you can ask for their amazing omelet brunch instead of their famous key lime pie. This makes a win-win for both parties: they have an outlet for their culinary love; you are able to enjoy their offerings without sacrificing your sugar abstinence.

You're Not Your Thoughts

Your mind can amaze you in its insistence: how, one day, after months of sugar free living, you'll be in the grocery store, and your mind starts screaming at you about how much you just have to *have* an ice cream sandwich. Or a piece of cake at your co-worker's wedding. Or pie on Thanksgiving.

It's important to remember that you are not your thoughts. Thoughts are just that: thoughts. They're like clouds in the sky, or the weather: they come and go, and change often.

You don't have to believe your thoughts. You don't even have to listen to them.

So if you suddenly get the thought that you'll die without that ice cream sandwich, you can nod politely and say, "Oh really?" And then ignore it.

You are beyond your thoughts. You are beyond your emotions. If you're feeling sad and craving a chocolate bar, you don't have to obey that feeling. You have a million different ways to respond to that feeling of sadness.

The real you is the observer, the one who questions your thoughts and emotions. The real you is much wiser, who can hear the petulant demand for ice cream, smile and say, "I care for you, and we'll be okay without it."

You Don't Have To Be Everything To Everybody

When I first gave up sugar, it changed not only my life, but the lives of those around me. Changing the way I cooked, changing the foods in the house, changing my daily habits altered the balance of power in all my relationships.

Suddenly, I wasn't so amenable to baking, or to sacrificing my needs for other people's. I made my daily exercise a priority. I made my regular mealtimes a priority. I made sleep and self care a priority.

This meant standing up for myself, asking for help and support, and setting boundaries on what I was and wasn't willing to do.

When friction results, it's easy to blame sugar abstinence as the cause of the problem. But the real issue is not whether or not you eat sugar, but the expectations of your role as a member of your family.

If your family is upset and irritated, have patience and compassion: of course they're upset. You've disrupted the status quo. It's expected that it will take time for everyone to adjust to the new you. If you feel selfish taking so much time for yourself, give yourself patience, honesty and compassion. Listen to what they're saying.

Are you truly neglecting your family? Or are you simply claiming a few hours for yourself? Or you bullying others, insisting that things are always done your way, or are you taking into account your family's opinions, too? Only you will know the answers to these questions.

You may seesaw back and forth for a while. I know when I first started setting boundaries, I went from one extreme - where I had no boundaries, and said yes to everything - to another, where I set up walls, refusing to do anything. My husband was very gracious to me during this time when I was often quite obnoxious to be around, I was so high and mighty in my "me first" self-righteousness.

I share this with you as an example of what not to do. I certainly am not proud of my behavior, even as I understand it.

And yet I think I had to go through this period in my life to sort out the difference between self-care and selfishness. I had to veer too far to the extreme of "me, me, me" so that I could find the middle way - honoring my needs alongside others'.

Let Go Of The Need for Approval

In living a sugar free life - a lifestyle that is different from the way the vast majority of people live - it's important to feel confident about your choices. Otherwise, it's easy to be dissuaded by other people. If you're someone who needs other people's approval, if it's hard for you to live in a way that is different from what's considered "normal," you'll eventually succumb to eating sugar, because eating "abnormally" is too uncomfortable for you.

Be confident about your decision to give up sugar. Be okay with your decision without having other people be okay with it, too. The only person who needs to approve of your sugar abstinence is you, you and you. What other people do or think is irrelevant.

If you abstain from sugar, you *don't* eat like everybody else. While, yes, more and more people are trying to eat healthier, and while, yes, there are other sugar free people out there, giving up sugar completely means that you are eating in a much different way then the majority of your neighbors, friends and family.

They may tease you about your eating habits. (I've been called Herb mother, a health nut, a rabbit, and have been teased constantly about my "weird food.") You need to be able to cope with this teasing; to laugh and shrug it off. It's not personal. But your eating habits make you different, and those differences make some people uncomfortable. They deal with their discomfort by poking fun.

We all want to belong, to feel like we're a part of the tribe. One of the ways we cohere as a people, as a culture, is through food. We break bread together - the word companion means, literally, "with bread"; we gather at the table to celebrate holidays, birthdays, and family togetherness. We share sweet times with sweets.

If you're consciously choosing to eat differently, people may feel like you're rejecting these bonds that unite us. It's no different than other lifestyle choices, like not having TV, or homeschooling your children instead of being a part of a public school system.

Focus on the ways that you are alike; on your similarities, not your differences. Join your friends and family at the table. Break bread with them: share their company, even if you don't share all of their meal. Laugh with them. Let their jokes roll off your back. Don't get hooked. As you lighten up and laugh at yourself, as you show your family nonjudgment and respect for their eating choices, hopefully, that attitude will return to you.

7

Chapter Seven

EXTRA HELP FOR THE HOLIDAYS

While it may be easy to resist sugar during the flow of your daily life, holidays can be a different story. This is because holidays are something that we share with others. They are communal celebrations, and with the dinners and gatherings and parties and celebrations come lots of expectations - yours, your family's, your husband's, your in-laws, your mother's, your children's.

Choosing to do something different than "normal," bucking tradition, skipping what was always done in holidays past can be seen as a betrayal. This is because of those unspoken, lofty expectations. When you skip the cookie swap, you're not just giving up the cookies; you're breaking the rules.

Holidays are also tricky because of the memories they carry. Every Christmas I pine for sugar cookies with icing and sprinkles. Physically, I don't crave them, but the little girl in me who used to bake cookies with her grandma every Christmas does.

There are solutions. Like other aspects of your sugar abstinence, they usually involve advance preparation, clear communication, and creative alternatives. Here are tips and tricks that help me navigate the holidays sugar free:

Saying No To Offers Of Sugar

There will be many, many times in your life when you will be offered sugar. You will have to find ways to say no in a kind and courteous manner. This does not mean that you have to lie, talk yourself blue, or offer up the twenty different reasons why you don't eat sugar. You can simply say, "No, thank you." That often suffices.

If it doesn't, it's important to recognize that people can handle the truth. Often, we tiptoe around the truth, disguise it, and hide it in an effort to spare someone's feelings. But people are stronger than we give them credit for. People can handle the truth. If your grandma is insistent on getting you to eat her apple pie - *But you always loved my pie! I made it just for you!* - you can gently say, "Grandma, thank you for the lovely pie, but I don't eat sugar."

While yes, grandma may be disappointed, she can handle your honesty.

I spent decades giving considerable time and mental energy to protect the feelings of those around me. While this may be well intentioned, it often backfired. While I may have protected other people's feelings, I did so at a high price. I exhausted myself by trying to keep everyone around me happy. I seethed with resentment when I cared more about other people's feelings than my own - resentment that I often channeled into a sugar binge.

The truth is that you can't make everyone around you happy. Saying yes to sugar won't change this. While eating your grandma's apple pie may keep the peace today, what about tomorrow, when she's offering cookies? Or what about when she's angry that you're leaving after a short visit?

We can't spend our lives holding the balance for everyone around us. If you are a people pleaser, someone who will do anything to avoid conflict, you may find that it's difficult for you to say no to sugar if it means ruffling feathers. But you have to make the choice: you have to be willing to put your own needs for health above your need for accord.

I'm not saying that we should steamroll over other people and have no consideration for their feelings. I'm saying that keeping everyone around us happy is an impossible, miserable job.

Conflict is inevitable. We don't always agree. Hopefully, you won't create discord every time you say no to sugar. But if you do, be willing to accept that consequence of living sugar free, rather than using that as a reason to break your sugar abstinence. Remember: everyone, eventually, will get over it.

What Do You Love About the Holidays?

Think about Christmas, Valentine's Day, or birthdays. What do those holidays mean to you? Are they about connecting with family and loved ones? Are they about feeling loved? Are they about feeling special? Are they about connecting with your religious or spiritual beliefs? Are they about giving to others? Are they about connecting with your community?

When you've identified what values or needs holidays serve in your life, then you can brainstorm about ways of meeting those needs without sugar. We often use sugar or food as a substitute, or a conduit - a way of meeting these needs in a simple manner. So we share a dessert as a way of fostering feelings of family togetherness; we have birthday cake as a way of celebrating our love for someone.

But we can find ways to foster these same good feelings…without the sugar. Instead of sharing birthday cake, maybe you take turns sharing what you love about the birthday girl or boy while eating strawberries in fresh whipped cream. Instead of eating dessert after Thanksgiving dinner, start a tradition of having everyone at the table share what they're thankful for.

Holidays are, primarily, about love. They're about finding ways to connect with friends and loved ones, near and far. Removing sugar from the holidays doesn't change this. You can still convey your love for your family members, even if you don't contribute your typical Christmas baking. You can still feel others' love for you, even if you don't eat their Christmas baking. Find other ways to connect without the sugar, so that the richness of your holidays is amplified, not depleted.

Rethink Your Image of a "Perfect" Holiday

The holidays are a time of huge internal and external expectations. It's easy to hold a mental image of the perfect holiday, and then feel disappointed when it doesn't hold true.

One way to ease this disappointment is to uncover the essence of your needs. What is a "perfect" holiday to you? Describe it. Then ask yourself, what needs are being met by that perfect scenario? Is it connection, community, joy, creativity, play, hope, beauty, or love?

When you're aware of your needs, when you're aware of the essence of what you want, then you can flex and bend and find ways to meet your need in a myriad ways. If you typically met your needs with sugar, you can think of other, healthier alternatives - new ways to meet the same need.

So, for example, if your need is for connection with friends and neighbors, perhaps you can arrange a caroling outing, instead of participating in the annual cookie exchange. Or, if you like to feel close to your grandma, and you achieved that closeness by baking from her famous pie recipes, how about recreating her famous roast, instead? There isn't one right answer, there's never just one way to meet your needs, but many possible solutions.

Find Creative Alternatives

I love Christmas baking, but choose to make bath salts, Christmas cards, and wreaths instead. I meet my needs for play, creative expression, and the pride that comes from making something myself, without facing the temptation of raw cookie dough and icinged sugar cookies.

If you typically made fancy cakes for birthdays as a way of celebrating your creativity, go ahead and continue making them: just be okay with the fact that you won't get to eat your creation. Or, how about using your creative talents to make a spectacular piñata, instead? Bring a watermelon to the 4th of July barbeque instead of ice cream. Trade juicy love letters with your partner at Valentine's Day instead of chocolate. Your options are as unbounded as your creativity.

Voice Your Preferences

Many of us fear that speaking the truth is rude, impolite, and will hurt other people's feelings. I've learned that people are more understanding than we think. I'm *not* advocating insensitivity or rudeness, but too often, we remain silent instead of speaking up for ourselves. I know it takes courage to abstain from eating your mother's famous strudel, or to tell your husband that you won't sample the chocolates he gave you for your birthday. But the flip side - ignoring your truth in order to be more socially acceptable - hurts more.

There are ways to lovingly communicate your needs in order to minimize hurt feelings. The best way I've found to do this is to communicate your love and acceptance of the other person, even as you say no to their request or offering. So, for example, my grandma will undoubtedly offer me a piece of apple pie at Christmastime. Here's what I can say: "Oh, grandma, I love that you are so considerate, and that you took the time to bake something special for the holiday. I love that about you. But I'm not having pie tonight. Can I have a cup of tea instead?"

If my grandma persists, I can keep gently repeating my message. Eventually, she'll see that I mean it when I say no. And while she may be disappointed, she can also get over it. Or she might not even notice, as she's busy serving pie to everyone else.

Let Go of What No Longer Serves You

Tradition and ritual are meant to serve you, not keep you bound in servitude. We often keep up with outdated traditions out of a sense of duty and familial guilt. Can you release a tradition that no longer speaks to your life right now? Do you want to skip the Christmas baking? Do you prefer not to have a cake on your birthday? Would you prefer to skip dessert at your dinner parties? One of the quirks of being human is that we feel like we can't change our minds. We think that decisions, habits, traditions are set in stone. But you always have a choice. No, or "not this year" is an option.

Create different traditions. For example, I don't have a cake on my birthday. My family sings to me and I blow out a candle that's been placed in my dinner - usually in a juicy, sizzling steak. Same effect, same joy, but sugar free.

Keep Up Your Self-Care

Keep up with your good habits - eating regular meals; eating breakfast; eating protein at every meal; getting adequate sleep; exercise. These things are crucial for maintaining your sugar abstinence, especially if you're traveling or spending part of the holidays with family, where you're on their schedule.

Honor What's Sacred to You

We often keep up with certain family traditions, not because we want to, but because we believe we're expected to. This is where the ties of tradition turn binding, like a straitjacket. Tradition can be a beautiful thing, but only if it serves you.

If you're driving yourself mad baking dozens of cookies every Christmas - cookies that you won't get to eat - recognize that it's okay to let the tradition go.

Too often, we keep the peace at our own personal expense, only to feel frustrated when we end up making (and eating) a batch of brownies in order to stave off our spouse's disapproval. A joyful sugar abstinence means finding ways to communicate our feelings, to negotiate conflicts with our loved ones, to find solutions that meet our needs, as well as another's.

As you release traditions that feel like joyless obligations, you create space to cultivate those traditions that *do* feel meaningful. Celebrate your most beloved holiday traditions so that you're not eating sugar as an inferior substitute, as a way of eating your disappointment. Does Christmas not feel like Christmas unless you go caroling? Sledding? Watch holiday movies? Make time for these activities.

In the busyness of life, we can lose sight of meaning, purpose, and true connection. We scratch the surface of the holidays, and then, when January comes, we feel let down - how did it pass so soon? - because we didn't pause deeply enough to enjoy it. Make time for the holiday traditions that speak to you, so that your tank is filled; so that your holiday feels "full." Even if it's only for 5 minutes a day, find a quiet time when you can reflect on what the holidays mean to you. Bask in the feelings of goodwill, peace, gratitude, and love. These intangibles are what we're really trying to find in the tins of fudge.

Make Peace with Letdown

Much of my holiday stress and sugar bingeing came from my attempt to stave off holiday letdown: that moment when the presents are all unwrapped, the Christmas dinner is eaten, and I feel like a deflated balloon. We all experience this emotion; it's a natural release after weeks of build-up and anticipation. I've found that there's no way to escape this feeling, although that hasn't stopped me from trying.

I would try and avoid this feeling by adding "more." The closer I got to Christmas day, the more anxious I felt about not having enough presents for my children. But this feeling isn't really about presents, but about trying to avoid the letdown when all the presents are unwrapped.

Overeating and overbuying are both attempts to stave off the inevitable lull of after Christmas letdown. We fill our plates and lives to the brim to avoid feelings of loss, letdown or a void.

Whether we like it or not, January comes. Honor the transition - the ending of a season - instead of avoiding it/denying it/burying it with sugar. Can you think of January traditions that you can implement, that will help ease your sadness? I use January to attend to household organization (what better time than when it's cold outside?), dreams for the New Year, and something fun.

Find awareness. Recognize when holiday letdown is driving your behavior to eat Christmas cookies, buy more gifts, or say "Yes" to something that you really don't want to do.

Keep the Love, Release the Sugar

"Sugar is not love," Kathleen des Maisons said, although it often feels like it is. When we subtract the sugar, are we also subtracting the love? Find ways to harbor a loving emotional connection at holidays without the sweet stuff.

Reflect back upon your childhood, and think about how much of your holiday celebrations revolved around sugar. This was true in my life: Valentine's Day meant chocolates; Easter, a huge, chocolate filled Easter basket; summertime was lots and lots of trips to the ice cream parlor; Sundays were a family trip to the donut store; my birthday, a huge cake, pop and candy; Halloween, a pillowcase full of candy; Thanksgiving and Christmas, pies, cookies, and special Christmas chocolates. Sugar was one way my parents showed that they cared. It was often how my friends showed that they cared. It was often how my grandparents and aunts and uncles showed their care.

We can show that we care without relying on sugar. In fact, sugar stumps our creativity. It keeps us from expressing our true feelings. It's so much easier to buy our child a sucker and watch their face light up, than to take them to the park and spend an hour playing with them. Sugar is quick, easy, and usually cheap. It also tastes good, which is why we rely on it to bring us joy and to communicate our love for one another.

Yes, it takes more effort to pen a love letter to your spouse instead of stopping by for a box of chocolates. Yes, it takes more effort to sit and console a grieving neighbor instead of just dropping off cookies. Yes, it takes more effort to come up with fun birthday rituals instead of focusing on the cake.

But while sugar tastes good, it's benefits aren't very long lasting. In fact, sugar can make us feel worse. By contrast, the benefits of sugar free connection are huge: the time, care, and attention you bestow upon your family and loved ones will come back to you, in deep, close, loving relationships.

Keep the fun; omit the sugar. Even though I limit my family's sugar consumption, we still enjoy lots of holiday fun. The key - here comes that word again - is creative alternatives. So, while my family holds an Easter egg hunt on Easter, I fill the plastic Easter eggs with some candy. But I also use nuts, money (they love this!), stickers, and other small toys.

Instead of exchanging chocolates, my children and I held a Valentine's Day tea when they were little, with strawberries and cream, little sandwich squares, tea and sliced fruit.

For Halloween, my family has given out fresh popped popcorn and hot apple cider: this was a huge hit in our neighborhood, particularly as Halloween is usually very cold here in Montana. Instead of stuffing my children's stockings with candy, I get them things like scented soaps, bath gel, roasted nuts, a fresh orange (this makes me feel very *Little House on the Prairie*), fancy pens and pencils, new drawing pencils, little journals or notebooks, and gift certificates for things like a date with Mom or Dad.

Don't Tempt Yourself with Holiday Goodies

If it's too tempting for you to have holiday goodies in the house, don't buy them. For years, I bought my Halloween candy on Halloween itself, as I knew that I would eat it if I kept it stored in the pantry for several days beforehand. You can also buy candy that you don't like, so you aren't tempted to eat it. Or you can give out nonsugar treats, like stickers or glowsticks. If stashing your home with Christmas cookies and candy canes will be too tempting, think of non-sugar treats you can set out, like roasted nuts, or shelled nuts with a nutcracker.

Use "Fairies" and other Creative Options for Halloween

My children go trick or treating on Halloween, and enjoy some candy on Halloween night. But that evening, the Halloween fairy visits our home, taking the rest of the candy with her. In its place, she leaves a small gift, such as a coloring book and crayons, a book, or a small toy. (She usually leaves one last piece of candy for each of the children to enjoy the next day.)

While I know this story may sound cruel, my children love the Halloween Fairy, and look forward to her annual visits. (They even leave her tender notes.) I share this story with you to show you that there are ways of minimizing candy's importance at holidays, even while participating in the holiday fun.

You Don't Have to Eat Holiday Gifts

If someone gives you chocolate, you don't have to eat it. If your elderly neighbor bakes you cookies, you don't have to eat them. If your mother-in-law bakes you a birthday cake, you don't have to take a slice.

Easier said than done, you may say. But so often we care more about the other person's feelings than our own. Be gracious; thank the other person for the gift. And then set it down. Untouched. Understand if they're miffed, or if their feelings are hurt.

But don't take it personally. Let it go. This is about you; and your sugar abstinence, remember? This is about your choice to abstain from sugar. That doesn't mean that everyone in your life will join your crusade. Your friends, family and neighbors can offer you sugar till the cows come home. You can still graciously decline.

At times, I've asked to take a gift home with me to share with my family.

This makes the giver feel good and yet I don't have to eat it right there - a win win for both parties.

8

JOYFUL SUGAR FREE LIVING: PUTTING IT ALL TOGETHER

The longer I travel on my journey out of sugar, the more I notice an interesting paradox. On the one hand, I am even more committed to sugar free living now than when I first started. I am more and more willing to leave the drama and self-sabotage of sugar behind.

At the same time, I've relaxed. I am much gentler towards myself with sugar, food and my weight. I don't label sugar as my enemy and feel so strident about defending my eating choices. I look at sugar more objectively, as perhaps someone who was allergic to a food would look at it. It's a limit I accept without the accompanying angst of, "But I want to eat it!" riding alongside with it. I think this comes from the healing nature of time.

I'm more accepting that other people may not approve of or like how I eat – and that their opinion is entirely okay.

In many ways, I'm unatttached. Sugar has faded more into the background, not because I don't care or because I'm in denial, but because I've integrated my sugar free decision into my daily life. It's mostly second nature now.

I'm not as fearful about slips back into sugar or as strident about "I will never, ever, ever eat another bite of sugar again." I appreciate that it's a practice, that life is imperfect, and stuff happens.

That being said, I don't use this unattachment as a "what the hell" excuse to eat sugar. I apply myself wholeheartedly to my practice, as I also accept that I won't always practice perfectly.

When I do slip – like the raisin binge that I'll discuss shortly – they were points of learning and reflection, not the end of the world. I trusted myself to dust myself off and come back to center.

I share this with you so that you can feel assured that the initial challenges do eventually give way to new habits. It won't always feel so uncomfortable. Like anything, what we practice becomes easier, more second nature, over time.

I suppose what I'm saying is focus on growth. Focus on growth, on learning, on listening. Focus more on these things than how many days you've been sugar free, or how much weight you've lost, or any of the externals. We can't always control the externals. But our attitude? Our heart? Our growth? Those are in our influence.

Focus on living each day the best you can, with as much grace, levity and compassion as you have to offer. It's all any of us can do.

As you leave this book and perhaps embark on your own journey out of sugar, I'd like to summarize the themes that I've explored in this book. In my humble opinion, these practices are what enabled me to separate from sugar – and what keep me in a joyful sugar free state today.

They are what made my journey out of sugar a greater lesson about living – what I can apply to challenges beyond ice cream and chocolate.

1. Will power is not enough. True motivation comes from the seed of compassion, from unconditional love.

When I first wrote this book, I was on the tail end of a decade long quest to get off sugar.

I was fairly confident that I had done enough inner work to be free from this sugar nemesis. I had come to a place of acceptance that I couldn't eat sugar and have inner peace at the same time.

So you can imagine how flummoxed – what the heck happened? - and discouraged I felt when I went back to sugar in February of 2010, nearly 3 years later, in a raisin binge. (You can read about my experience on FirstOurselves.org, in the article "That darn can of raisins: a February binge.")

Underneath the analysis – what went wrong? – there was also a bitter judgment. I felt like a tremendous fraud. I mean, I *had* written a book that tens of thousands of people had read about giving up sugar. I was so disappointed in myself.

So instead of looking at my sugar binge as an opportunity to learn something very valuable about myself, my first reaction was to slam the door, try and hide the mistake, and do everything I could to get back on track.

If you cover up a mistake before anyone else sees it – and before the consequences pile up – you can almost pretend that it never happened. Denial is a sneaky opponent.

I really, really wanted to hide. Fortunately, I live with other people, in particular a husband who calls my bluff. He said, "Write about it."

His trust in me – and his belief that I am more than a raisin binge – was the courage I needed to go deep inside, once again. Sigh. (Do you get as tired as I do of the lesson after lesson after lesson?)

What I uncovered was something so valuable that it prompted me to pull this book off the market, go back, revise it, and alter my message.

I learned that I will never be "done," cured, healed in the way my mind would like to be – cured in the sense that I won't have to stay awake and open and curious and be willing to open the door of the room that scares me the most.

I learned that I can't control life. I learned that trying to control or eliminate every possible craving is an exercise in futility. And I also learned that I was still approaching my sugar abstinence from a place of fear.

Control, will power and discipline were how I stayed sugar free for several years, until that fateful day when a can of raisins (yes, an entire can) called my name.

Deep down, I didn't trust myself. I still thought that I had to control my behavior. I was fearful and anxious – not so anxious that it tripped me everyday, but enough that when life got hairy, and stressful, the anxiety seeped out. It seeped out and wanted soothing and raisins were how I responded.

What I really needed, beyond any surface healing with food, was kindness. I needed to believe that I was good – that I wasn't a bad child with "bad" impulses. I needed to know that I was more than my bingeing.

This belief in a "bad self" creates a false story that says, "Because I'm bad and can't be trusted, I have to be watched." You control, tame, stuff, hate, loathe. You treat yourself like a criminal that will do wrong at every turn. All your behavior is observed through this lens.

This is exhausting. It's like walking a tightrope, where we're always watching for a slip.

 We lose faith in our natural goodness. We look at our untrustworthiness, our hopelessness, our history with sugar and we feel terrible – that who we are is horribly flawed. What we are most terrified of is mercy – which is why we keep chastising ourselves and whipping ourselves into shape and scathing ourselves with our inner critic.

We're terrified that if we forgive ourselves and show ourselves compassion that we're giving ourselves license to keep indulging in our painful behaviors. We think that holding ourselves kindly – instead of healing the painful patterns – will perpetuate them.

How wrong we are. It is compassion that softens are hearts and makes us responsible – able to respond. It's what helps us find the inner goodness and courage and wisdom to let go of the bingeing, the comfort eating, the sugar, the attempts to control, the fear – and find freedom.

To find consistent change – change that sticks and lasts – and to find helpful change – change that feels good – we must start with unconditional love. We must start with compassion. We must believe that our inherent nature is goodness.

We must find compassion for ourselves even when we're at our worst – especially when we're at our worst. It's no different than parenting a child. When our children act out, do we punish them and send them away? Or is it then when they most need our love and tenderness?

It is our care that softens our children. It is our care that softens our behavior as well.

It is unconditional acceptance, and unconditional love, that loosens the chains of self -sabotage. It is unconditional love that softens our habitual patterns that cause us so much pain. It is unconditional love – not will power, not control, not fear – that creates the deep shift in how we approach sugar.

It softens our self-absorption and helps us remember, "I am not my faults. I have divinity inside." We live from a greater perspective, a broader sense of who we are. This opens up all sorts of possibilities about how we can respond, how we can behave, how we can be.

2. Accept the daily journey while getting on with your life.

I have a wise friend who raised a severely disabled daughter. As many of us do when faced with a challenging situation, she looked for resources to help her and attended support groups. At first, the group was invaluable, but after awhile, the support group was no longer helpful. Eventually, she stopped going because she left feeling worse than when she arrived. She said, "People can stay stuck in recovery or struggle when they need to move on."

We can also stay stuck in "recovery" and the struggle to get off sugar. We can forget that it's only one stage in the journey – something to move through, not live in. As you heal from sugar, yes, you will go through recovery. There will be moments of challenge and intensity. You will have valleys to climb out of. But don't stay there.

I love how Kathleen des Maisons describes this – after getting off sugar, you need to "get on with your life."

"Getting on with your life" does not mean that you eat whatever you want and go back to the sugar. That's not healing. It's denial.

"Getting on with your life" doesn't mean that you start skimping on your self-care because you're healed now.

Repetition is a great teacher. Life is changing and dynamic, an ebb and flow. We have to get comfortable with the fact that the daily nature of our journey – honoring, meeting and caring for our needs - will never end.

You get on with your life by adjusting with the growth process. As you feel more separation from sugar, you let yourself enjoy your freedom instead of being fearful about what's around the corner. You let yourself relax and live. You trust in your ability to take care of yourself. You rest in being.

3. Honor your needs.

In order to stay sugar free, I have to care for my physical, emotional and spiritual needs. And I have to do this over and over and over again. We will never stop doing these things. It is precisely these things that keep us sugar free. It is precisely these things that make us feel nourished, cared for, connected to others, loved, and secure.

What we sometimes do is see these things – the repetitive nature of self-care - as a sign of weakness. We think, "Oh, I'm strong enough to fake it." I can get by without eating breakfast, I can skip lunch; I can go 6 hours between meals. We walk around pretending to be someone who can eat like a bird and feel just fine; we act like one of those people who don't need to eat (or sleep, or rest, or just plain need) – we are so above that – regularly to feel good.

We act superhuman, like we don't need regular nourishment, because we think it's a sign that we are healed. That we are over sugar. And we are so desperate to be over sugar.

When you stop doing the things that keep you sugar free, you will find your journey gets much, much harder. You will find that you start craving sugar. You will feel ungrounded as you no longer have the assurance and calm that a regular, rhythmic way of eating and caring for your needs brings you.

Our resistance to caring for ourselves comes from our dislike of our very human neediness.

As human beings living in physical bodies, we have basic needs. And one of our most basic needs is for nourishment - food, water, vitamins, minerals, air.

There is something so tender about our humanity, our fragility, about the way our bodies need. If I stop feeding my body on a regular basis, I will feel terrible. Low blood sugar, irritability, and hunger pangs will follow. If I stop eating long enough, my body would eventually die.

If we don't water a plant, it dies. If we don't feed the dog, it will die. And yet we feel like our hunger, at a basic level, should be contained. Minimized. (You even see this in diet and nutrition books as a sign of progress - "I don't feel hungry anymore," as if hunger is a flaw to be eliminated.)

I'm here to encourage you to embrace your hunger. To embrace your humanity. To embrace your basic needs that require eating regular meals, at a regular time, every day.

I want you to look at wanting to nourish yourself with food, at its most basic level, as something good. As something that can be trusted. Yes, we may take this desire and turn it into something else, as a coping mechanism for life's pain that takes on a life of its own, consuming our lives. Anything to excess is harmful. But nourishing your body is, at its root, an act of care. An act of kindness. An act of love, motivated by love.

Instead of labeling yourself as high maintenance, or looking at yourself as someone who should "need" less, care for your neediness. Have compassion for your humanity, for your human body that gets hungry and tired on a regular basis, for your feelings, for your tender human soul.

4. Honor your limits. Mourn what you can't change.

We are all met with limits in our lives. We have a limited amount of time in a day. We can only eat a limited amount of food – there's only so much our stomachs will hold. Most of us have a limited amount of money. We have a limited amount of energy.

We have to make peace with our limits. We have to accept them and then pick and choose accordingly. You must choose. You have to decide – how do I want to live in my body? Do I want to eat sugar? Do I want to be free from sugar? How do I want to feel physically?

When you choose, you accept a limit. Choosing one thing means saying goodbye to the alternative. This can hurt. Choosing to live in one house means you can't live in another; choosing to spend an afternoon with a friend means you're not with your family; choosing to stay home for the holidays means you won't see the relatives that live out of state.

To avoid this pain, we try and have it both ways. We try and avoid facing our limits. We try and work around them. We try and avoid the loss.

For example, we do this by eating the sugar and thinking that we also won't have the natural consequences of eating the sugar – like cravings, mood swings, and irritability.

The choice and the consequences go together. Honoring limits and acceptance go together. It's the only way we can grow up and find freedom.

We may have to let go of our shoulds about how we think life should be – or how we think we should be - and accept what is. We may have to accept that eating a food we're allergic to or that we're sensitive to – like sugar - causes painful repercussions. Fighting this limit only prolongs our pain.

As long as we are avoiding loss, we will rail against limits. We will fight them. We will try and work around them.

We can even do this in extreme ways – by throwing up our food, by compensating for our overeating with a punishing workout, or by fasting to make up for a binge. It's our way of trying to have it both ways – to eat whatever we want and not gain weight. It's how we try and sneak our way around the natural consequences.

We spend a tremendous amount of energy resisting pain and avoiding it. It is actually more painful and more work than turning towards our pain and accepting the limit. But it means facing what we've been trying to avoid.

Once we face our limits, we can mourn. We can grieve. We can feel our sadness or anger over the limit.

It's what allows us to accept the "no" and move forward.

It may sound silly – mourning something as simple like sugar – but letting ourselves feel our feelings creates the soil for us to let go. We open the space to create a joyful sugar free life versus a resentful one.

As you mourn what you can't change, you actually integrate your decision in your brain.

We grow up and realize, while there is much I can't change, there is much I can. There is much that is in my power. It's the emergence of acceptance – of finding ways to create our happiness in these new circumstances.

It's how we start to love the foods that love us back. We let go of our resistance and open our minds up a crack with curiosity – I wonder what I can create for dinner with more whole foods? I wonder if eating more whole foods will change my taste buds? I wonder if I'll get to a point where the junk food won't even appeal to me that much anymore?

So we may not eat sugar.

But, boy, oh, boy, look at what we can eat. Look at how we can give ourselves pleasure. Look at the abundance we do have. It is the doorway to gratitude.

5. Feel your feelings. Honor your many selves.

Ah, feelings. For those of us who turn to food, we often have a multitude of ways of avoiding our feelings. We hide in work, food, TV, entertainment. We go to our heads and intellectualize. We focus on "Why?" instead of feeling our hurt. We blame others. We lash out. We react to our feelings instead of actually feeling them.

It is certainly much, much, much easier to eat an ice cream cone than to dig into our emotions.

For most of my life, I have been very anxious about "negative" emotions. Anytime I am less than perfect, any time I feel any negative emotion like sadness or fear or loneliness, anytime my depression and anxiety rears its head, anytime I fall off the wagon with food or sugar I dig for a reason: Why? Why am I feeling this way?

I dig for a reason because I feel guilty. I feel ashamed. I feel like it's all my fault. I feel like I've been bad and I am full of judgment and I am waiting for the punishment.

I was always trying to stop, change, improve my feelings – I felt like such a bad person for feeling sad, or lonely or jealous.

The mindfulness and compassion practices have been crucial for me in befriending my feelings. These practices helped me turn towards my feelings instead of running from them.

When I feel myself reaching for food, or some other coping mechanism to avoid my feelings, I step back. I pause. I ask myself, "What am I feeling? What's here?"

I breathe. I sink into my body. I label what I'm feeling – "Tightness in my throat. Knots in my belly." I label my feelings, "Sadness. Grief. Fear."

I sit and hold my feelings, peeling through the layers. I show my feelings care. I welcome them. I soften my resistance. I literally sit and tell myself, "I care for you. I care for this suffering."

As I tenderly, lovingly hold my feelings, as I show myself care, the feelings soften. My whole body softens in response. I cry my tears. I feel my sorrow. I truly feel my feelings – which hurts – and which is also very cleansing.

And yet I also create feelings of spaciousness and lightness and peace – because I'm no longer judging myself. I'm no longer blaming myself. I'm able to sit with all my feelings of, "This is not how I wanted it to be."

It is this tender holding, this awareness and compassion, that enables me to determine what to do next, to take the wise steps to care for myself, to do what needs to be done to nourish my body appropriately, whatever that may be – to stay off the sugar, to put away the dinner plate, to go for a walk instead of graze the pantry.

Opening to my feelings and needs has helped me in that I'm not fighting against my feelings or thoughts like I did. This is where the control piece comes in. I don't feel like I have to protect myself against these "bad" feelings by trying to be good all the time in the way that I did. I no longer look at myself as if I were a criminal who always has to be watched lest she be caught being "bad" – feel jealous of another woman, bingeing at night in front of the fridge or losing it with my kids. I am learning to trust my goodness.

How this translates with food is this - I practice sitting with a craving when it comes up and welcoming it as something to teach me, as something to open my heart to something tender and vulnerable and precious inside.

This isn't always easy for me. In fact, it's often terrifying and it can hurt. And I don't practice perfectly. Sometimes I go for the food. But the more I practice, the more I can move through the fear and have compassion for that, too, and I can hold myself tenderly when I do go for food, knowing I'm doing the best I can.

For me, my journey is really about befriending myself. If I get nothing out of this journey through my food stuff beyond that, honestly, that's enough for me – because I can feel that glimpse of softness, the freedom of self-acceptance that I have been searching for in my life for so long. In my life, freedom from food comes from this freedom of self-acceptance.

When we care for, love and accept all parts of ourselves, we are fully alive, fully human, experiencing the wide range of human emotions, needs and feelings.

6. Honor your growth process.

We carry around "shoulds" about how growth should be easy, quick and feel good. We also carry around many judgments about how we should be feeling as we change. Because we are tender human beings, and because we all want to feel good and be free of pain – naturally - we label anything uncomfortable as wrong. Bad.

True change hurts. Not in the way that beating ourselves up or judging ourselves causes suffering, but in a, "I am in the birth canal and this is uncomfortable" way of hurting.

When we label and judge all pain as, "Something is wrong with me. I must have done something wrong or I wouldn't be feeling this way," we fight against the growth process. We turn the natural pain of growth into suffering, compounding it further so that we stay stuck.

Shifting your habits can be uncomfortable. It can hurt. When I am feeling a powerful urge to overeat and I don't bite the hook, I sob sometimes – I moan and cry and weep because I hurt so badly and all I want to do is ease that pain.

A teacher of mine once told me, "No one ever said enlightenment is easy." We do ourselves a disservice when we expect it to be easy – and when we expect ourselves to navigate all our challenges pain free.

Having awareness about the nature of our pain – what some call the pain of pushing through versus the pain of giving up – can soften our resistance to it. We can accept, "Oh, this is just change. This is just growth," without personalizing it into pain against us.

We just keep putting one foot in front of the other. We trust that as we move forward we will have everything we need to make the next step, and the next, and the next. We try to stay present instead of projecting into the future – "But how will I survive my birthday without a cake?"

The truth is, you will be a different person on your birthday than who you are now. You may get to your birthday and have no desire for cake. Or you may be at peace with your desire for cake and your intention not to act on it.

We just don't know how we will be feeling a month, six months, a year from now. Honoring our growth means taking steps forward as we also do our best to stay present, to stay right here.

Your journey out of sugar will teach you everything you need to know about yourself. It is your personal instruction manual, the book of you. Everything you need for the journey, everything you need to stay sugar free is included in that journey. It's all in you. It's not anything you need to manufacture or grasp after. It's both the seed and the fruit of growth.

Love the journey. Love what it teaches you. Love and honor and care for your growth process – and yourself – as something precious and valuable and good. This creates a safe container for you to unfold.

7. Slow down.

Most people in our modern culture are addicted to speed, productivity and achievement. Our self worth is tied to what we produce, what we see, how much we do.

So slowing down, spending more time on our health and basic care, scheduling in time for rest, quiet and meditation, and creating pockets of "fun time" can conflict with our hard driving goals.

Interestingly enough, I've found it virtually impossible to stay sugar free and be addicted to productivity at the same time. When I start overeating, it's almost always a sign that I am doing too much. I don't even question it anymore. I just know, "Oops, I ate three plates at dinner tonight. Where is my life too full?"

Giving up sugar meant reexamining my approach to myself. I realized how hard I pushed myself – how often I ate to keep myself going when what I really needed was rest. I saw how pushing myself depleted my reserves and my ability to sit with my feelings. I saw how I then justified overeating and eating sugar because I was pushing myself so hard. It was my built in binge excuse, why I deserved it.

I will admit – quieting my inner taskmaster has been very, very challenging for me. I've been a type A overachiever for much of my life. It was terrifying to let go of my high expectations. It was a roller coaster ride of back and forth for many years. I resisted this step over and over again. It was only after hitting rock bottom with several depressions that I was willing to concede defeat.

It's a path I'm still learning and traveling on today – finding the balance between having enough external stimulation in my life and too much. Quieting my anxiety when I want to go, go, go and yet I know I need rest or centering.

Slowing down has meant accepting life's losses. It's meant sometimes saying no to things I would like to do. It's meant accepting life's limits, once again – that I have a limited amount of time and energy, and that overspending it doesn't somehow gain me an extra bonus – it just leaves me depleted and tired.

I really wanted to believe those who said I could have it all, who said that I didn't have to choose. I look at people who have it all and I wonder – how do they do it?

I wonder, and I'm curious, and I'm also more comfortable with my more balanced, relaxed approach. I appreciate what slowing down has brought me, including my very health. Then, over time, I've gained inner peace, sanctuary, self trust and inner resilience. The need to control the externals has greatly softened. This then creates less of a need to hurry up and get it all done, because there is less out there I'm trying to control. Letting go and slowing down feed each other and go hand in hand.

When we rush, it's a sign that we're seeking something beyond this present moment to feel okay. It's a sign that we haven't made peace with enough. This moment isn't enough, so we have to rush to get somewhere else. This bite of food isn't enough, so we want more. This plate of food isn't enough, so we want sugar.

Why are we rushing? Where do we expect to get to? Why do we rush to reach the end, to get there as quick as we can, which, after all, is death?

8. Remember who you are.

When we're entrenched in painful patterns like overeating, bingeing, and chronic dieting, we start to believe that we are our faults. We lose sight of our essential goodness. The real work in healing from food is not eating differently. It's seeing ourselves differently.

It's a paradox of honoring our humanity – and caring for our tender, human selves – and honoring our spirituality. We remind ourselves that we are not just our human bodies and feelings and emotions.

We all have a soul, a deep, wise one within. We connect with this deep, wise aspect of ourselves when we stop running and diving into sugar. We create a relationship with ourselves.

This relationship helps us connect with our virtues – our strengths and moral courage – and our values – those aspects of the Divine that speak to us. It's how we bring our values up to the surface of our life, entwined in our daily behavior.

I often say, "You have everything you need, right now, to heal." That's because all of us have that Divine seed. We all have access to those higher qualities. We each can connect with our grace, compassion, mercy, courage, discipline, honor, integrity, honesty and love.

When we remember our essential goodness, we start to trust ourselves again. We believe that we know how to take care of ourselves – which translates into different behavior.

When we recognize that we are not the bingeing self, we find the ability to stop the bingeing. It is no longer who we are. We create spaciousness to respond differently to the siren song of fresh baked cookies.

9. Pay attention.

Sugar binges don't start all at once. Neither does illness, stress, burn out, or exhaustion.

It all starts with a trickle. You may hear a little voice niggling at you, saying, "I'm not getting what I need. Feed me. Nourish me. Care for me." This is the voice of your body saying – help.

Your body, your wise, wise body – will tell you what it needs. The voice of our body is not to be confused with the voice of craving – the voice that says we will die without a cookie, a sugar hit, a drink, a smoke, a joint, a dessert.

Pay attention to these messages. Pay attention to your body when it calls out for help. They are little reminders saying, "Remember me?"

When you're tired, when you're feeling like life is too hard, when you find yourself tip-toeing into bad habits, sit up. Take notice. This is your body telling you that you need to go back to grounding. That you need to go back to doing the things that helped you get off sugar in the first place. It's message is ultimately helpful and kind – because it is trying to help you take better care of yourself.

A sugar binge can serve the same purpose. It's an invitation to dig below the surface, to turn off the blame and judgment (which never helps) and inquire: What's really going on? What needs aren't being met? What feelings am I avoiding feeling?

That's when the real work begins.

10. Release the suffering.

While our needs don't end, and our journey doesn't end, our suffering can end.

That's how I define healing – ending the suffering. What is suffering? Judgment. The feelings of, "I can't change, and I hate this part of myself, and I'm terrified that I can't do this." The self loathing - "I'm such a horrible person because I'm so fat, because I am so gross, because I stuff myself to oblivion; I'm worthless; I'm so ashamed of what I've done to my body."

Suffering can be in our heads – the neuroticism and overcontrol and food policing and constant stream of thoughts about what you should and shouldn't eat, the anxiety about every single thing that you put in your mouth.

Each layer of suffering creates a barrier in your life, a barrier that keeps you from experiencing all the joy and love and mystery that the world has to offer. We're not present when we're caught in our suffering. We're cramped and crouched and tight. We respond to others from this cramped space and then add to our pain when we lash out, overreact, and hurt those we love.

Where I've seen people struggle is that they stop the healing process after they have their sugar abstinence – they heal their physical suffering, but don't heal their emotional, spiritual, or mental suffering. They remain as stuck and as imprisoned as they were when they were eating sugar.

And because they are still stuck, they are not truly free.

Sugar is a rabbit hole that leads you to your deepest being. The journey of healing our sugar addiction will lead us to our deepest pain, to our deepest suffering. It is an invitation, an opportunity, to heal deep seated beliefs, locked emotions, and hidden (and not so hidden) pain. This is, ultimately, why my sugar addiction changed my life.

We're afraid to look at our suffering. We're afraid that if we look at it, like the fairytales of old, it will bind itself to us. We'll turn into stone.

But healing is the ultimate irony. It is by looking at our suffering and turning towards it that we become free.

Dive into your stuff. Open the door. It's all there, waiting for you.

9

Chapter Nine

HELP FOR FRUSTRATION
AND DISCOURAGEMENT

As you move forward into your sugar free life, I want to give you one last final gift.

Right now, you're probably feeling excited, eager to begin, ready to conquer this sugar thing once and for all. Your motivation is running high.

At some point in your journey, this may shift. You may become discouraged. You may want to give up. You may think this is impossible, that it's too hard, that you can't do it, and you may even wish that you'd never read my book in the first place.

Don't panic. This is part of the journey. It's a part of the healing. I would even say it's a necessary part of healing.

As someone who is walking on the same road, who is walking on the same sugar free path, what can I offer you?

If I had to encapsulate the journey of becoming sugar free in one word, it would be this: persistence.

Did you ever see the movie *Finding Nemo*? In the movie, Nemo's dad is swimming across the ocean to rescue his son, and he meets a fish, Dorie, who joins him on his mission. As they swim across the ocean, encountering obstacle after obstacle, Dorie sings, "Just keep swimming. Just keep swimming. Just keep swimming, swimming, swimming…"

That is what I want to say to you, wherever you find yourself on this journey.

Just keep swimming.

Just keep going. Keep showing up.

Some days, that's all you can do, is to keep showing up. Even if you binge on sugar. Even if you go back to sugar after a 2, 3, 10 or 50 week abstinence. Even if you vowed this morning to stop and find yourself knee deep in chocolate by the afternoon.

Just keep going. Just keep swimming.

I once heard a story about a woman who'd spent years trying to give up alcohol. Her alcoholism was so powerful that she wasn't even able to stop drinking while being pregnant or after receiving several DUIs.

And yet, she did it. She has been sober now for several years. How did she do it? She said, "I firmly believe that as long as you are breathing and as long as you're doing the work, you can heal."

It's true. It's never too late.

All of those voices that tell you, you can't change, this is too hard, this is impossible, you'll never make peace with sugar are wrong. As human beings, we have the ability to change. We have the ability to make difficult choices, to face the discomfort and pain of saying no to a sugar craving in the short term so that we can feel the joy of sugar free living in the long term.

The other day I saw a sign on my gym's bulletin board from a personal trainer. She said there are two kinds of pain in life: "the pain of pushing through and the pain of giving up." The pain of giving up is always more painful than the pain of pushing through.

When we stumble on our journey, we start to think that maybe we're the exception to the rule. That maybe everyone else has something we don't have to say no to sugar. We think that we don't have what we need to heal. We feel the pain of pushing through and we think this pain means stop, when it's actually a sign of progress.

We take the stumbles – which are a normal, natural part of the journey; which are actually signs that we are moving forward – as a reason to give up. We search for something out there to complete us, to enable us to heal, not recognizing that everything we need - the inner strength, wisdom, courage and openness - is already inside us.

Inside of every one of us, we have a wise, knowing soul, an inner parent, who longs to be sugar free. It is this part of you that prompted you to read this book. It is this part of you who has sought out information on becoming sugar free. It is this part of you that tells you, gently, "No, you don't want that," when you pick up the chocolate chip cookie. This is also the part of you that recognizes when you slip – it's the part of you that says, "Hey! I really don't want to be doing that!" And then it's the part of you that helps you get back on track after the slip.

Do you see? You already have this person inside you. Your job is to grow that person until her voice is the one that you hear when you are confronted with birthday cake – not the voice of your inner child who says, "But I want to eat it!" It is this part of you who comforts that inner child and says, I will take good care of you. I know you want the cake and it makes you sad that I'm saying no but you're going to be okay.

Do you feel this essential pain, this necessary pain of loss that you must feel to say no to sugar? That is the pain of pushing through. And the pain of going back to sugar can be the pain of pushing through, too, because each time you go back to sugar and experience the pain of bingeing and sugar cravings and addiction this can cement your desire to be free from sugar – if you let it. It can remind you that, "Yes, every time I eat sugar, I overeat it, which is why I want to abstain." It can fuel your motivation, and be the pain of pushing forward rather than the pain of giving up.

Pain is not a sign that the journey is going awry. It is not a sign that you have fallen off the path. It is the pain of pushing through. It is the pain of giving birth to the new you that is emerging in the world.

For those of us who embrace life as a spiritual path, we can mistakenly believe that living out our deepest purpose will be easy - that following our intuition will make all our problems go away. We want smooth sailing. So when we struggle on our journey to become sugar free, when it's hard, we judge it, label it as "bad" or as a sign of "failure," and interpret it as, "Something's wrong with me. Something's wrong with being sugar free, because if it was 'right' for me it would be easy."

Here's what I've learned on my lifetime journey out of food: following your heart's calling is not a vaccine, an inoculation against pain. Sometimes pain is a part of the journey, as we rid ourselves of old, painful patterns and beliefs. Yes, it hurts when I want to eat sugar and I say no. But that pain is much, much less than the pain of eating the sugar, suffering the binge, and suffering the heartache of dishonesty – of knowing that I'm not living out my truth.

As the old adage goes, pain is a part of life; suffering is optional. And I deeply suffer, and cause those around me to suffer, when I eat sugar. That, in a nutshell, is why I am committed to my path of being sugar free. And that is why I stay committed, and I persist, and I keep swimming, day after day, even when I go back, even when I slip.

So how can you embrace the necessary pain, the necessary losses of living a sugar free life? For me, it all comes down to story: what story are you telling? What story are you feeding? How are you interpreting your journey?

Are you using your sugar abstinence as a way to feel sorry for yourself, as a way to feel like a victim? Or are you using your sugar abstinence as a way to honor yourself, to love and care for yourself? Is it a story of courage and breaking free, or a story of woe and despair?

I like to take the story one level deeper. Do you remember the classic myths? All the fairytales you read as a child? What they all have in common is the hero's journey. The prince or princess has to slay the dragon, face the enemy, conquer their inner demons, before they reap their reward.

It's the same for you. You are on your own hero's journey.

That's why this journey is a practice, a discipline. We do it everyday. We get the opportunity to practice every day. No one ever said it would be easy. Are we willing to show up and accept the challenge?

And are you willing to show up day after day, however long it takes? Are you willing to give yourself however long you need to grow and heal?

If you look at nature, everything grows in its own due time. We don't expect a sapling to bloom into a full blown tree overnight. We don't

expect an athlete to pick up a sport and win a gold medal the next day. So why do we expect such impossibilities for ourselves?

We decide, yes, I want to give up sugar. And then we are decimated when we stumble. Instead of recognizing, wow, this is going to be an adventure, and this is going to take some practice, and looking at it with some humor – oops, there I go again! - we use our slips to judge ourselves – *I can't do this; I'll never be able to change; Everyone else is doing so much better than I am. I'm just a piece of crap.*

Instead, give your emotional, physical, and mental bodies time to heal. To adjust. To change. Your emotions, mind and body need to catch up to the intention that you hold to be sugar free. They are growing into it. Honor this growth process by giving it the space and love it needs to take hold. Be a loving container for your growth. Don't yell at it when it's putting down roots and giving rise to a tender bud because it's not yet a full grown plant.

Recognize that the back and forth process of abstaining from sugar to eating sugar and back to abstaining from sugar is how you grow. How you change. How you become sugar free. It's a sign that the roots are taking hold. Because you are sugar free part of the time now, when before you were never sugar free.

Eventually, what will happen is this: as you persist, as you keep showing up, you get tired of banging your head against the wall. You get tired of banging your head against the wall, eating sugar, and feeling terrible afterwards. You get tired of banging your head against the wall – trying to eat sugar moderately – expecting a different result. You finally get, on a heart level, not a head level, that this is not working. You realize how insane it was to keep trying to eat sugar and expect to feel good at the same time.

And so you shift. You adapt. You change.

You realize, "I don't want to feel the pain of a binge. I don't want to go back and forth." You stop banging your head against the wall. You realize, I have a choice. And you take a leap forward. The binges becomes less frequent. You feel more peaceful about letting sugar go. And you practice. And you persist. And you keep showing up. And you keep swimming. And your plant grows.

You deepen the cycles. You practice them again. You find new walls to bang your head against, and then you release those. You adapt. And you go around and around and around and find deeper and deeper levels of healing.

So don't take the chaos as a sign of "there's something wrong." There is always chaos before order. Spring is full of chaos. And then comes summer. And then your harvest.

Just keep swimming. Keep showing up. Keep showing up through all the cycles, knowing you have what you need to shift, knowing that you're right where you need to be, knowing that growth is the whole point of the journey. As long as you're growing – and we grow from chaos and "mistakes" as much as from smooth sailing and "success" – you're practicing. You're coming home to your true nature.

10

Chapter Ten

FINDING THE DEEPEST FREEDOM

It's been several years since I first embarked upon this path of sugar free living. As I mentioned in earlier chapters, my journey has included many ups and downs – even after I was certain, *absolutely certain*, I had come to a point of certain recovery and would never eat sugar again.

My return to sugar after publishing *Overcoming Sugar Addiction* represented a low point in my life. I felt embarrassed, ashamed, frustrated and lost – deeply lost. Looking back, it was the proverbial blessing in disguise, although if you would've told me this at the time, I would've punched something! I was in so much pain and felt so discouraged by my struggles. The last thing I wanted to hear was that it was good for me.

That season of my life – a period of three years when nearly everything fell apart, including my sugar abstinence, my confidence, my health, my relationships, my finances, my home and community, and my basic sense of safety – forced me to look inside and face some underlying beliefs that I had carried for years.

Opening to the full journey

During that dark time, I confronted my desire to control – in particular, my desire to control my experience (my feelings, emotions, thoughts, weight, sugar abstinence and more) so that it was always positive, happy and "good." I felt humbled to learn that I was still using my sugar abstinence as an escape, a way of avoiding my feelings and the entire, messy breadth of my human experience. I wanted to control/look good rather than grow up and mature. (Sigh.)

Those rock bottom years forced me to walk the messy path of growth and process. If I wanted to be free, I had to allow – to open to all my feelings, all my needs, all my emotions, and all experiences, pleasant and unpleasant. I had to open to the full, wondrous, beautiful mess. (A woman I know put it this way, "Grace tracks in the messes.") I had to grow up and relinquish my childish beliefs.

Did I have the courage? Did I believe in my strength, that I could handle this? Was I willing to open to grace, to let go of control and childish things, to accept life on its own terms?

The shame of "It's all my fault"

Yesterday I was being interviewed for a radio show and the host asked me, "Why do you think you went back to eating sugar after all that time? Were you eating for comfort? Were you bored?"

I thought about it for a moment. Yes, I was definitely eating for comfort – I was going through a very hard time and was hurting. But what was I needing comfort *from*? That made me pause.

The answer surprised me. I was needing comfort from *me* – from the judgments in my head that said it's all my fault that I was hurting, that I should've been able to keep my sugar abstinence going, that I was the cause of all the pain in my life, that it was all my fault that I was so sensitive, that I should've been able to change who I was, that I should've been able to erase my personality and challenges with all my inner work. I was embarrassed by my woundedness, my immaturity, and my very vulnerability.

I was feeling shame. Guilt. Blame. Self-judgment – I had been blaming myself for the pain in my life, for my hard time, for being sensitive and sugar sensitive in the first place! I was blaming myself for being *human and imperfect, a work in progress.*

Over and under responsibility

Some of us tend to be under responsible – we blame others for all the pain in our lives. Or we may go to the opposite extreme and feel over responsible – we blame ourselves for all the pain in our lives. In my experience, most people who struggle with food and sugar addiction – what one student in my classes called the "nice girl's addiction" – fall in the over responsible category.

What we want to do is find balance. Yes, some of the pain in our lives is something we can change, and worth changing; much of it is not. We use our wisdom to discern the difference. If we're someone who tends to be over responsible, we find balance by practicing self forgiveness and compassion – seeing the 10,000 factors that lead to any action, decision, or situation.

When we see how the confluence of many, many factors and many, many people's behavior leads to certain outcomes, we step back a bit from this idea that "it's all my fault." We open to interdependence.

Interdependence is not just sharing our burdens with one another, coming alongside each other in help and support. Interdependence is sharing our common responsibility for the world we each contribute to – recognizing that our behavior affects others and that their behavior affects us. Saying one person is responsible denies our interconnectedness.

Compassion is the mercy that stops the pattern of self punishment, of beating ourselves up for "causing" every bad thing in our lives. With compassion, we can look honestly at what we can change – the portion that is our responsibility – and surrender to what we can't.

Rather than judging ourselves for our pain we see it clearly (compassion isn't denial!) and then care for it wisely. We forgive. We let go of self blame. We find mercy.

Failing the spiritual test

Learning how to care rather than control (and to find compassion rather than criticize) is my ongoing edge of growth. I'm a very eager, conscientious person who tries to live with integrity and purpose. I'm also a seeker, someone who likes to search for understanding and freedom.

Deep down, I thought that if I just prayed enough, meditated enough, and did enough of my inner work that my life would line up exactly as I wanted; that I would be rewarded for my work and that I could erase my human condition. I thought that I could change anything about me and make life exactly as I wanted.

So the fact that my life wasn't lining up according to plan felt like a giant judgment against me – proof that I was failing Life 101. Because I wanted to live so conscientiously, I set the bar even higher for myself than for other people. Other people could make mistakes and do C+ work, but because I was trying to walk this super-conscious path, mistakes weren't okay for me. I should know better. I had to *do* better. I had to make straight A's.

With the bar set so high, I felt like a failure when I couldn't keep up. And then when I couldn't be perfect – good and gentle and loving all the time – I felt ashamed, and scared! Now I was really going to get it. I was going to get nailed for doing life "wrong" and "attracting" all the wrong things with my negative thinking and pain.

Ouch.

If I did less than 100%, I wasn't enough. If I didn't look like a serene spiritual master, I wasn't enough. If I was in process I wasn't enough, because I had all this messy humanity that kept tumbling out – deep insecurities, anxiety, a tendency towards depression, loneliness, and all my fears about not belonging, being too much, not fitting it, and being unlovable.

Moving from hubris to humility

What I was moving from was hubris – I create my own reality. I'm in charge. What I was moving to was humility – the Divine is in charge. (In 12 step groups, this is known as turning life over to your Higher Power.)

There is a relief in this. When we accept that we are not in complete control we open to grace – a revealed path that may hold gifts and mercies that we wouldn't have discovered on our own. We learn that maybe we don't know what is best; maybe letting go and trusting the river of life works better than forcing the flow.

We also open to forgiveness, to a lightness of being. This journey of humanity can be so complex – who among us can do this perfectly? Not having to be in control is a grace, a mercy, and not a punishment.

Moving from hubris to humility meant opening to some difficult truths. I felt humbled to appreciate that even my good heart and good intentions could not create a life free of pain; rain falls on us all. I felt humbled to learn that I will always be a work in progress, and that includes acknowledging my limits, challenges, and imperfect humanity. I felt humbled to release my belief of God as Santa Claus, handing out rewards, or God as rigid judge, handing out punishments.

I felt humbled to appreciate that my controlling, super high expectations were creating all this tension, a tight rope I had to walk perfectly – a tight rope that perpetuated the very tension I was trying to soothe; a tight rope that sent me back to sugar.

Abandoning myself in the face of pain

During that painful time, I wasn't thinking about caring for myself, being kind to myself – I just wanted to eradicate all my bumbling, tender humanity so I could be happy like everybody else. I imagined their lives as carefree – free from the cares and worries that plagued me. I was self absorbed in my suffering and believed I was the only one hurting. No one else had problems as big as mine. I felt small and separate and alone.

I felt shocked to see how judgmental I had been towards myself. Sure, when life was smooth sailing and going according to plan, I loved myself. I trusted my path. I trusted myself. I trusted the Divine.

But when life got hard and painful? I turned on myself. I blamed myself. I abandoned my heart. I railed at God. I was filled with a judgment of, "You should be able to control this." The fact that things were out of control was proof of my failure.

It's interesting to observe this line of thinking, because I certainly wouldn't blame you if your house caught on fire, or if your pet ran away from home, or if an employee emptied out your bank account. Somehow, those things qualify as "acts of God" in my book, or something outside of your control. But because my pain was inside of me, and seemed to come from me, I felt like it should be in my control.

I blamed myself for being a human being, for feeling pain. I blamed myself for feeling difficult emotions and having painful thoughts. I blamed myself for having patterns of behavior that were less than helpful.

Despising my ugly, messy parts

This blame and feeling of "not okayness" made me feel like an outcast inside my own heart. How could I be at rest and feel enough if there were these giant parts of me that were forbidden, that had to be eliminated or cut out? How could I feel good about myself while despising a part of myself?

It's no wonder I went back to sugar. Who wouldn't, in the face of such pain, such judgment? The most painful part of my hard time was not the hard time itself. It was the pain of blaming myself for it, of abandoning myself when I was hurting.

It's the same judgmental attitude I carried towards my sugar sensitivity, my sensitivity, and my tender nervous system that can struggle with depression, low self esteem and anxiety.

Sure, depression is not fun. Yes, being sensitive can feel overwhelming at times. Anxiety brings challenges. But those things are manageable if I have love. With love, they can be the very ground for my growth and acceptance. With love, they may even become endearing. With love, I find freedom in the midst of challenge.

Without love, they are excruciating. Without love, I feel flawed and deficient and definitely not okay – and I will do crazy, compulsive, addictive things to try and soothe this suffering.

Feeling shame for how we're made

It is this feeling of shame and unworthiness – that I'm bad because I'm sugar sensitive, that it's proof that I'm deficient, that my humanity is something inherently shameful – that keeps us from caring for our sugar sensitivity. It's why we feel uncomfortable asking a waiter if there's sugar in a dish, or passing on dessert, or doing any number of things that help us feel strong, capable, healthy, and nourished.

There is a part of us that is still arguing with our human reality, that feels a judgment of, "But it shouldn't' be like this! I shouldn't need to be sugar free. I *should* be able to eat like everybody else!"

When these shoulds come to the forefront of our minds – when we start believing them to be true and turn them into expectations – they play havoc with our behavior. We obey the shoulds and not reality.

We stop doing the very things that help us cope, those things that support ourselves and help us feel better – like eating a low sugar diet

– because doing them is a shame trigger, a reminder that, yep, we've got this tender humanity (with some tender human limits) to care for.

Dropping blame

I think we all blame, as it's part of our human nature. Our blame can be very subtle, but it is still present. Our blame arises in our shoulds; in the ways we think we should be different. We feel blame in the tension we feel in our bodies when we make a sugar free meal, or when we say no to dessert. The tension represents our resistance, our feelings of, "No, it shouldn't be this way…"

We feel this tension of, "It shouldn't have to be this way," like we are bad or somehow at fault because we can't eat sugar. We feel guilty because we have to care for ourselves in this way! Often, there is a voice in our heads that tries to persuade us that we should be able to control; we should be able to manage the unmanageable differently, or at least better!

I was reminded of this voice when my cat died last week. It was very sad, and came suddenly. After she died, my mind was spinning with thoughts of, *"If only I had taken her to the vet sooner, if only we hadn't moved and given her this trauma of relocating, if only we hadn't gone away for Christmas (we might have noticed that she was starting to slow down), if only, if only, if only…. I could've prevented this from happening."*

Then I started spiraling into feelings of guilt – did I love her enough when she was alive? Did I appreciate her? I should've done more for her. I should've held her more…I should've taken more pictures….and on and on…..

All these thoughts, at the most basic level, were believing two things to be true: If only I had done more, I could've prevented her from dying. I should've been able to control it. I'm bad/not enough because I couldn't stop her from dying. **I'm bad/not enough because I can't stop the pain in life.**

And I'm bad/not enough because I'm human and I don't have time for everything. I'm bad because I sometimes forget to sit with my kitty because I'm caught in my to do list and the hubbub of life or trying to pay the rent.

As I saw these beliefs I realized – oh, my goodness – they've been running my life. Running my life and causing me to doubt my goodness at every turn.

Feeling our feelings to let go

So I let go. I started with grieving. I felt very sad to lose a family member – sad for myself and sad for my family. I let myself feel my grief without the layers of, "The grief is my fault." I felt my powerlessness – the hopelessness of losing something I dearly loved. I released the self blame, the guilt, because those are subtle ways to try and grab power, to try and control what is uncontrollable – the randomness of life, the sorrow of losing pets (and more than pets.)

And I felt my raw grief, my raw powerlessness and I wept. I wept and accepted – this hurts. I surrendered to it. And in my surrender, I let go of this idea that it was my fault that she died. I surrendered to what is – my beloved cat dying – even as I hurt; even as I wanted it to be different.

And in that surrender, I found freedom. I found peace.

Letting go

During that hard time, the Divine was teaching me to let go of the reins. This is what I mean by letting go of the reins: letting go of the externals; letting go of my need to have the externals meet my expectations.

Our expectations often show up like this: *Well, if I give up sugar, than I'd better be a size 8, and I'd better look really good, at least 10 years younger than other people my age, and I'd better be free from any illness and anxiety, and I'd better look like that woman in the gym who is super fit and bounces her way through the super, super hard class, and I'd better be sexier, and smarter, and more together...*

Or our expectations can show up like this: I should be able to control the pain in my life. I should be able to prevent the things I love, like pets and people and projects and even ideas, from dying.

Letting go is trusting life's natural course, which includes pain, loss, and death as well as joy, rebirth, and life.

Letting go is surrendering our attachment to the externals; to the results.

Letting go is doing something kind for the sake of doing something kind; not because we expect a payback for our virtue. I love my cat because I love her, not to get something back from her. I love myself by not eating sugar because it's kind to my body– not because it's a guarantee that I'll have some magic formula for happiness. I love my family and friends not because of what they can do for me, but because I just love them, and appreciate them so.

We let go by finding new ways to relate to sugar, food, our bodies, our needs, our emotions, our wounds, our desires, our thoughts, our challenges, our limits, our problems – all of our humanity. The key word is relate, which connotes a relationship. How are we relating to our struggles? Hopefully, these new ways of relating will become more and more kind.

With sugar, letting go looks like this: am I being sugar abstinent to get a reward? Or am I doing it as an act of love, because it helps my body and heart thrive? Am I doing this just because I want to guarantee a certain outcome? Or am I willing to do this just because my heart says it feels right?

I appreciate that this is not easy. I know how much I want to guarantee the externals and control the outcome. Letting go asks much of us.

Loving unconditionally

In my experience, all healing is grounded in love. It was love that saved me. It was love that helped me climb out of that hard, hard time. It was love that brought me to my knees, to question my belief of, "It's all my fault that I'm hurting."

I sat with that belief for two years. It kept arising, hitting me in the face, as my difficulties spiraled around me. I wept as I felt the pain of that belief. I wept as I felt the isolation, the judgment.

Little by little, I brought that belief up to the light, to love. I kept asking – and wise friends kept reminding – "What if that belief isn't true?"

What if it's not my fault? What if my life isn't here to be controlled, but to be cared for? What if my problems and hard times and challenges and "flaws" are not something to despise, to cut out, to resolve, to transform, but something very tender, very precious – something that's asking for my love?

When I open to those beliefs, my entire self – my heart, my soul, my mind – softens and relaxes. It's like a giant exhale – ahhhhh – as the tightness in my belly and across my chest melts and finds warmth. I find mercy. I come home to the truth of who I am – a loveable, precious, tender being – and I feel peace.

I cry but I don't cry tears of sorrow, but tears of relief; of homecoming. Tears of remembrance : ah, yes, this is truth.

The path of healing

I think we heal by shedding false beliefs. Beliefs that we've probably carried our whole lives, and that no longer serve us. Beliefs that say we're unworthy, at fault, not okay, being punished, unlovable. Beliefs that say we should be in charge.

We shed these beliefs by forgiving ourselves for carrying them. We shed these beliefs by forgiving others for teaching them to us. We shed these beliefs by forgiving God for allowing the process.

We forgive, we let go, we release what isn't true, we surrender to what is, and we come home.

What unconditional love looks like

On a ground floor, nuts and bolts level, love looks like this: when we're feeling anxious, we can allow our feelings to be there. We can speak kindly to them – "There, there anxiety, I'm here. You're safe with me. I've got you now." We can choose to show care rather than control.

Love looks like this: When we notice that we're craving sugar, we show acceptance rather than, "Go away feelings!" We allow the feeling to be there. We soothe our cravings with understanding and validation – "I know you want to eat that sugar, and I know it hurts to say no, and I will take good care of you. Let it all out. I'm here for you." And we allow ourselves to feel all our feelings of grief and frustration about what we're choosing not to eat.

Or if we eat the sugar, we love that. We care for the regret and upset tummy and reassure ourselves that we're here to learn, and that learning is messy. (To paraphrase psychotherapist Rollo May, we can learn equally from mistakes and successes.)

Love looks like this: not giving up on ourselves. Giving ourselves everything we need to thrive, all the time in the world to heal, and 10,000 different options, if that's what it takes.

Love looks like this: allowing all our feelings.

Love looks like this: When we catch ourselves judging ourselves, and not allowing our feelings, we can love that, too. We allow our not allowing. We forgive ourselves and say, "It's okay. I know this isn't easy. Try again next time."

Love looks like this: welcoming the hurt little child inside and caring for that tender child – not suppressing it in drink, drugs, food, denial or diversion.

Love looks like this: not abandoning ourselves when we're in pain.

Love looks like this: talking very, very kindly to ourselves.

Love is allowing everything to flow through us without judging it as good or bad; without saying, "You can't exist, you must go away!" Love is opening to the full breadth of our human experience.

Love is staying with ourselves when we're in pain, just as we would want a good friend to stay with us if we'd hurt ourselves and needed comfort.

Love is fierce and brave. It is tender and sweet. It is nothing but kind. Love is opening our hearts and saying, "My heart is big enough. My heart is big enough for all of me."

Finding the deeper journey

Oh, Beloved, do you see the task before us? The task before us is not to control our humanity or to look at ourselves as if we are machines in need of new parts – if I just replaced this broken part, or got rid of this part of me, then I'd be fine.

The task before us is to love. To care for our tender parts with exquisite kindness – what I call growing human(kind)ness.

In his poem "St. Francis and the Sow," poet Galway Kinnell says, "sometimes it is necessary to reteach a thing its loveliness." This is kind. This is healing: relearning our loveliness.

Healing is not the externals, what we weigh, what we look like, or how many days we've been sugar free. Healing is not about the mind, the intellect, rationalization – coming up with rational reasons why we're lovable or good or kind. Healing is not intellectually getting, "Oh, I'm sugar sensitive" and then making a rational plan to carry this out.

Intellect, will power, and rationalization are not the problem and not the answer.

The answer, Beloved, arises within your heart. This is where we heal. What do you believe about yourself? Who do you think you are? Do you believe in your inherent worth, your loveliness, your goodness? Or do you blame yourself for all the "flaws" or challenges or pain in your life?

Healing is knowing your own loveliness, right down into the hollow of your bones; into every cell, into that cracked, broken aching hole in your heart that seeks, over and over, to find that fulfillment in sugar, in food, in something...

Healing is looking at that broken, aching hole and caring for it with such compassion, such tenderness, such kindness instead of blaming yourself for having it in the first place.

Why control leads to shame

So much of life is out of our control. We would rather feel guilty and beat ourselves up about how we should've done more than to feel this truth and surrender. And yet as long as we feel like we should be able to control life, we'll suffer. As long as we feel that we should be able to control our sugar sensitivity and eat sugar moderately, we'll suffer.

My friend Deidre uses this phrase to practice surrender – "It couldn't have happened any other way." Try that on. When I say it to myself, my whole being softens and relaxes. My heart unclenches and I feel relief. I let go. I come home.

Try that with your sugar sensitivity, or even the years you spent bingeing on sugar. "It couldn't have happened any other way." Do you feel relief as you drop the self blame? As you drop the idea, that somehow, you should've been able to do life differently – to be different?

Your sugar sensitivity is not meant to be controlled. It is *to be cared for.* Care for it with kindness, with heart, with compassion, and see if you can soften the blame, guilt, control, shame, feelings of "less than" or "too much."

Surrender into forgiveness

So if you want to become really free – free in your heart, in your mind, on the inside as well as the outside – surrender. Accept how you are made. Question those voices in your head that say, "You should be different." Question the shame that has you feel less than because you need to eat regular, sugar free meals (or whatever you need) to feel good.

We grow our human(kind)ness so that we can reach our potential – healing painful patterns, finding self acceptance and inner freedom, and increasing our capacity to give and receive love. It is this radical kindness that enables us to grow out of sugar and grow into our fullest selves. (Learn more about growing human(kind)ness in my follow up workbook, *Overcoming Sugar Addiction for Life*.)

We take it baby step by baby step. We grow into our fullest selves by letting go of judgment – in particular, the judgments we carry towards ourselves. I should be more….I should be less….I shouldn't feel…..I shouldn't think… ..I shouldn't be…I shouldn't have…..

We grow into our fullest selves by looking ourselves in the eye and saying, "I love how I am made. I love all of me."

We grow into our fullest selves by living this truth: I will care for this tender human vessel – just as it's made – with the most exquisite kindness that I can.

My focus is no longer on sugar. I know that sounds provocative, especially as this is a book about sugar abstinence! So let me explain. I don't mean that I'm flippant about eating sugar. What I do mean is this: sugar abstinence is not the ultimate goal, even though it's an important practice, and one I do my best to honor. (Yep, I'm still imperfect.)

The ultimate goal is care. Can I be kind to myself? Can I care for myself? Can I care for a body that is sugar sensitive?

Can I be gentle with myself?

This approach – to care rather than control; to grow human(kind)ness rather than will power, to understand rather than judge – is what shapes my sugar abstinence today. Yes, it's a lot messier. (But it feels a heck of a lot better!) Yes, I still make lots of mistakes. But kindness gives me the means to care for my mistakes rather than nail myself for them. And this edge is where I grow and stumble and forgive and celebrate each day.

It's where I meet you and extend my hand.

May I be kind. May I choose love. May I choose care. That is my daily prayer for me, for you, for every being.

FREE GIFT FOR YOU

Thank you for buying this book and for taking the first step to create a joyful, sugar free life.

I've recorded a special audio just for you on what I've learned about emotional healing, sugar abstinence, and self love. To access your free gift, go to http://www.sugar-addiction-book.com/bonus. Simply enter "sugarbook" to listen.

I wish you much joy, freedom, and peace on your journey.

In love and care,

Karly

BIBLIOGRAPHY

Brach, Tara. *Radical Acceptance*. New York: Bantam, 2004.

Des Maisons, Kathleen. *Potatoes Not Prozac*. New York: Simon & Schuster, 2008.

Frost, Robert. *The Poetry of Robert Frost: The Collected Poems, Complete and Unabridged*, ed. Edward Connery Lathem. New York: Henry Holt, 1969.

Gates, Donna with Linda Schatz. *The Body Ecology Diet*. Bogart, Georgia: B.E.D. Publications, 2006.

Gilbert, Elizabeth. *Eat, Pray, Love*. New York: Penguin, 2007.

Kabat-Zinn, Jon. *Wherever You Go There You Are*. New York: Hyperion, 2005.

Katherine, Ann. *Anatomy of a Food Addiction*. Carlsbad, California: Gurze Books,1991.

Neufeld, Gordon. *Hold On to Your Kids*. New York: Ballantine, 2006.

Neufeld, Gordon. *Power to Parent* video course, http://www.gordon-neufeld.com

Rilke, Rainer Maria. *Letters to a Young Poet*, trans. Joan M. Burnham. New

York: New World Library, 2000.

Rosenberg, Marshall B. *Nonviolent Communication: A Language of Life*. Encinitas, California: Puddledancer Press, 2003.

Ross, Julia. *The Diet Cure*. New York: Penguin, 2000.

Ross, Julia. *The Mood Cure*. New York: Penguin, 2003.

Seixas, Abby. *Finding the Deep River Within*. New York: Jossey-Bass, 2006.

Wiley, Eleanor with Caroline Pincus. *There Are No Mistakes*. San Francisco: Conari Press, 2006.

READING LIST

Books on sugar:

Get the Sugar Out: 501 Simple Ways to Cut the Sugar Out of Any Diet by Ann Louise Gittleman

Lick the Sugar Habit by Nancy Appleton

Little Sugar Addicts: End the Mood Swings, Meltdowns, Tantrums, and Low Self-Esteem in Your Child Today by Kathleen Des Maisons

Potatoes Not Prozac: A Natural Seven-Step Dietary Plan to Stabilize the Levels of Sugar in Your Blood, Control Your Cravings and Lose Weight by Kathleen Des Maisons

Sugar Blues by William Duffy

Sugar Shock!: How Sweets and Simple Carbs Can Derail Your Life...and How You Can Get Back on Track by Connie Bennett

Nutrition Books that I've found helpful:

Chakra Foods for Optimum Health by Deanna Minich

Intuitive Eating by Elyse Resch and Evelyn Tribole

Mindless Eating: Why We Eat More than We Think by Brian Wansink

Nourishing Traditions by Sally Kempton

Nourishing Wisdom by Marc David

The Crazy Makers: How the Food Industry is Destroying Our Brains and

Harming Our Children by Carol Simontacchi

The Diet Cure by Julia Ross

The Mood Cure by Julia Ross

The Slow Down Diet by Marc David

Ultra Metabolism by Mark Hyman

Books on overeating: *

Anatomy of a Food Addiction: The Brain Chemistry of Overeating by Anne Katherine

Eat by Choice, Not by Habit by Sylvia Haskvitz

Eating, Drinking, Overthinking by Susan Nolen-Hoeksema

Fit from Within: 101 Simple Secrets to Change Your Body and Your Life by Victoria Moran

Making Peace with Food by Susan Kano

Overcoming Overeating by Jane Hirschmann and Carol Hunter

The Zen of Eating by Ronna Kabatznick

When Food is Food and Love is Love: A Step by Step Spiritual Program to Break Free From Emotional Eating by Geneen Roth

Why Weight? A Guide to Ending Compulsive Eating by Geneen Roth

Women, Food and God by Geneen Roth

* Nota bene: Some books on overeating suggest allowing yourself to eat all foods in moderation. The authors believe that our labeling certain foods

as "bad" (like sugar) causes us to overeat them. I understand where they're coming from.

And yet…through trial and error, I learned that moderate sugar consumption doesn't work for me. It triggers my sugar sensitivity and leads to addictive patterns. So while I don't label foods, I do choose to abstain from sugar – not because sugar's inherently "bad," but because it makes my body feel terrible.

I think this is a subtle difference.

You can read books, seek out advice, and learn helpful approaches. And you can also drive yourself nuts trying to implement everything you read!

Your litmus test is always your body. How does eating this food make you feel? What about this kind of meal? Be okay with integrating several different approaches and making a custom plan for your body.

Be okay with disagreeing with an expert. You're the expert on your body. Take one idea from this book, one idea from another, and put together an approach to food that works for you.

ACKNOWLEDGEMENTS

Thank you to my teachers, those who paved the way and whose voices had a hand in my own healing. I bow to you in gratitude. All errors are my own.

Abby Seixas, Byron Katie, Carl Jung, Cheri Huber, Elaine Aron, Elisabeth Fitzhugh, Gary Zukav, Gordon Neufeld, Jon Kabat-Zinn, Kathleen des Maisons, Laurel Mellin, Marshall Rosenberg, Pema Chodron, Sally Kempton, Tara Brach, Thomas Moore, and Wayne Muller.

To all my personal healers, doctors and therapists who helped me navigate my way out of the sugar maze – I couldn't have done it without you.

To my family and friends, to the divine creator, thank you for believing in me, loving me and providing immeasurable physical, emotional and spiritual support. I want to especially thank my husband and children, who lived with me and loved me through my darkest hours.

May this book be a balm to your heart as you travel on the path of freedom.

May it bring you closer to your true nature, your inner goodness.

May you be healthy, happy, and free from suffering.

AUTHOR BIO

Karly Randolph Pitman has done it all when it comes to getting stuck in food. Her 20 year struggle with sugar addiction, bulimia, binge eating disorder, compulsive overeating, and body hatred - as well as her lifelong struggles with anxiety and depression - have been both her greatest challenge and her greatest teacher.

These struggles sent her on a healing journey into self compassion, self acceptance and unconditional self love. Karly synthesized these practices into a process she calls growing human(kind)ness™. Growing human(kind)ness is a map to heal the emotional roots of eating disorders and addiction, based in loving relationship and compassion.

Karly speaks about growing human(kind)ness across the country, sharing these tools with counselors, therapists, and those in recovery. Her dream is to create a world of compassion and belonging - where we befriend our tender humanity with greater gentleness and care.

Karly's the author of the best selling *Overcoming Sugar Addiction, Overcoming Sugar Addiction for Life, The 30 Day Lift, Heal Overeating: Untangled,* and *Heal Your Body Image.* You can learn more about Karly at www.karlyrandolphpitman.com and read her blog at www.firstourselves.org.

For more help on becoming sugar free, visit Karly at www.sugar-addiction-book.com. As our special gift to you, go to http://www.sugar-addiction-book.com/bonus to download a free audio on becoming sugar free. Simply enter "sugarbook" to access this helpful audio.

Karly lives with her family in Austin, Texas and Montana.